Your Relationships

Choosing Abstinence and Good Character

TEXAS

Teacher's Guide

D1410855

Linda Meeks
The Ohio State University

Philip Heit
The Ohio State University

Macmillan
McGraw-Hill

Table of Contents

The *McGraw-Hill* Companies

**Macmillan
McGraw-Hill**

Published by Macmillan/McGraw-Hill, of McGraw-Hill Education, a division of The McGraw-Hill Companies, Inc., Two Penn Plaza, New York, New York 10121.

Printed in the United States of America
1 2 3 4 5 6 7 8 9 079 09 08 07 06 05 04

Family Letter

Dear Parent or Guardian,

Your child's health class is continuing its study about relationships. As part of this study, the class will be using a supplementary book titled *Your Relationships: Choosing Abstinence and Good Character.* This softcover book contains information that is intended to supplement and reinforce the material in the classroom textbook.

Your Relationships is designed to help students make responsible decisions regarding relationships. In the eight chapters of this book, students will be exploring such topics as how to communicate effectively, how to develop healthful relationships with family and friends, how to understand the responsibilities of dating, and how to handle conflict in relationships. Students will also learn the signs of good character. Throughout the book, emphasis is given to students conferring with parents and guardians, following family guidelines, and making responsible decisions with parental accord.

As they explore the chapters, students will also learn about the changes that occur during puberty. They will study the male and female reproductive systems, the menstrual cycle, pregnancy, prenatal development, and childbirth.

Most importantly, *Your Relationships* reinforces the concept that abstinence from sexual activity is the expected standard for teens. Students will study reasons to practice abstinence and will learn how to avoid situations that might put them at risk, such as using alcohol and other drugs. Learning about the risks of teen marriage, pregnancy, and parenthood will help to reinforce the value of abstinence from sexual activity before they are married adults. Students will also learn facts about STDs, HIV, and AIDS, and how abstinence will reduce or eliminate their risks of becoming infected.

Thank you for your continued interest in your teen's health course. As always, please feel free to contact me if you have any questions or concerns about this material.

Regards,

Health Teacher

Carta a los Padres

Estimados padres o guardianes:

La clase de salud de su hijo(a) continua con el estudio de las relaciones. Como parte del estudio, la clase usará un libro suplementario titulado *Sus Relaciones: Escoger la Abstinencia y Tener una Buena Reputación*. Este libre con cubierta suave contiene información que completa y refuerza la materia en el libro de texto.

Sus Relaciones ayudará a los estudiantes a hacer decisiones responsables sobre las relaciones. En los ocho capítulos de este libro los estudiantes explorarán temas tales como: cómo comunicar efectivamente, cómo establecer relaciones sanas con la familia y los amigos, cómo entender las responsabilidades de salir con uno y cómo manejar los conflictos en las relaciones. Los estudiantes también aprenderán las señales de una buena reputación. Por todo el libro, se pone el énfasis en la importancia de que los estudiantes hablen con los padres o guardianes, sigan las reglas de la familia y hagan decisiones responsables con la ayuda de sus padres.

Al explorar los capítulos, los estudiantes aprenderán sobre los cambios que ocurren durante la pubertad. Estudiarán el sistema reproductor del varón y de la hembra, el ciclo menstrual, el embarazo, el desarrollo prenatal y el parto.

Lo más importante es que *Sus Relaciones* refuerza la idea que la abstinencia sexual es la norma esperada para los adolescentes. Los estudiantes aprenderán las razones por las cuales deben practicar la abstinencia y aprenderán cómo evitar situaciones riesgosas, como usar el alcohol u otras drogas. Entender los riesgos de casar, del embarazo y de ser padres cuando sean adolescentes ayudará a reforzar el valor de la abstinencia sexual antes de ser adultos casados. También los estudiantes aprenderán datos importantes sobre enfermedades transmitidas sexualmente, el VIH y la SIDA y cómo la abstinencia reduce o elimina el riesgo de infecciones.

Gracias por su interés en el curso de salud de su adolescente. Como siempre, por favor siéntase libre de ponerse en contacto conmigo si tiene cualquiera pregunta o preocupación sobre esta materia.

Les saluda,

Maestro(a) de salud

Correlations

Texas Essential Knowledge and Skills (TEKS)

Macmillan/McGraw-Hill Your Relationships
Correlated with Texas Essential Knowledge and Skills (TEKS)

For Health Education

Macmillan/McGraw-Hill Your Relationships, Grade 7–8

Health, Grade 7–8

(1) Health information. The student comprehends ways to enhance and maintain personal health throughout the life span. The student is expected to:

(D) Describe the life cycle of human beings including birth, dying, and death. pp. 38–46, 67–70

(2) Health information. The student recognizes ways that body structure and function relate to personal health throughout the life span. The student is expected to:

(A) Explain how differences in growth patterns among adolescents such as onset of puberty may affect personal health. pp. 41, 43–44

(C) Compare and contrast changes in males and females. pp. 38–46, 50

(D) Examine physical and emotional development during adolescence. pp. 37–46, 49

(3) Health information. The student comprehends and utilizes concepts relating to health promotion and disease prevention throughout the life span. The student is expected to:

(A) Explain the role of preventative health measures, immunizations, and treatment in disease prevention such as wellness exams and dental check-ups. pp. 41, 45, 57, 64, 67, 86, 88, 94

(B) Analyze risks for contracting specific diseases based on pathogenic, genetic, age, cultural, environmental, and behavioral factors. pp. 75–85, 88, 94

(D) Summarize the facts related to Human Immunodeficiency Virus (HIV) infection and sexually transmitted diseases. pp. 41, 43, 75, 85, 88–97

(4) Health information. The student knows how to research, access, analyze, and use health information. The student is expected to:

(D) Discuss the legal implications regarding sexual activity as it relates to minor persons. pp. 22, 53

(5) Health behaviors. The student engages in behaviors that reduce health risks throughout the life span. The student is expected to:

(C) Identify strategies for prevention and intervention of emotional, physical, and sexual abuse. pp. 22–23, 33–34, 41, 43, 54

(D) Identify information relating to abstinence. pp. 41, 43, 49–58, 91

(E) Analyze the importance of abstinence from sexual activity as the preferred choice of behavior in relationship to all sexual activity for unmarried persons of school age. pp. 22–23, 33–34, 41, 43, 49–58, 61–62

(F) Discuss abstinence from sexual activity as the only method that is 100% effective in preventing pregnancy, sexually transmitted diseases, and the sexual transmission of HIV or acquired immune deficiency syndrome, and the emotional trauma associated with adolescent sexual activity. pp. 15, 41, 43, 49–58, 75–85, 91

(H) Explain the impact of chemical dependency and addiction to tobacco, alcohol, drugs, and other substances. pp. 23, 33, 54, 66–67, 85, 92–93

(I) Relate medicine and other drug use to communicable disease, prenatal health, health problems later in life, and other adverse consequences. pp. 53, 66–67, 85, 92–93

(6) Influencing factors. The student understands how physical and social factors can influence individual and community health throughout the life span. The student is expected to:

(A) Relate physical and social environmental factors to individual and community health such as climate and gangs. pp. 15, 18, 50, 98

(7) Influencing factors. The student investigates positive and negative relationships that influence individual, family, and community health. The student is expected to:

(A) Analyze positive and negative relationships that influence individual and community health such as families, peers, and role models. pp. 3, 18, 20–22, 33, 51, 71, 98

(B) Develop strategies for monitoring positive and negative relationships that influence health. pp. 3, 18, 20–22, 33, 98

(8) Influencing factors. The student researches ways in which media and technology influence individual and community health throughout the life span. The student is expected to:

(A) Explain the role of media and technology in influencing individuals and community health such as watching television or reading a newspaper and billboard. p. 55

(9) Influencing factors. The student understands how social factors impact personal, family, community, and world health. The student is expected to:

(A) Describe personal health behaviors and knowledge unique to different generations and populations. pp. 15, 29, 34

(B) Describe characteristics that contribute to family health. pp. 16, 28–30, 53, 55, 64

(10) Personal/interpersonal skills. The student recognizes and uses communication skills in building and maintaining healthy relationships. The student is expected to:

(A) Differentiate between positive and negative peer pressure. pp. 18, 98

(B) Describe the application of effective coping skills. pp. 30–32, 34

(C) Distinguish between effective and ineffective listening such as paying attention to the speaker versus not making eye contact. p. 8

(D) Summarize and relate conflict resolution/mediation skills to personal situations. pp. 6, 9

(E) Appraise the importance of social groups. p. 50

(11) Personal/interpersonal skills. The student understands, analyzes, and applies healthy ways to communicate consideration and respect for self, family, friends, and others. The student is expected to:

(B) Demonstrate strategies for coping with problems and stress. pp. 9–10, 22, 32
(D) Describe methods of communicating emotions. pp. 4–10, 32
(E) Describe the effect of stress on personal and family health. p. 32

(12) Personal/interpersonal skills. The student analyzes information and applies critical-thinking, decision-making, goal-setting, and problem-solving skills for making health-promoting decisions. The student is expected to:
(B) Relate practices and steps necessary for making health decisions. pp. 13, 17, 28, 52–53, 56, 98
(D) Predict the consequences of refusal skills in various situations. pp. 52–53, 56, 98
(E) Examine the effects of peer pressure on decision making. pp. 13, 17, 28, 52–53, 56, 98

For English Language Arts and Reading

Macmillan/McGraw-Hill Your Relationships, Grade 7

English Language Arts and Reading, Grade 7

(7.7) Reading/fluency. The student reads with fluency and understanding in texts at appropriate difficulty levels. The student is expected to:
(B) Read regularly in instructional-level materials that are challenging but manageable (texts in which no more than approximately 1 in 10 words is difficult for the reader). pp. 2–101

(7.8) Reading/variety of texts. The student reads widely for different purposes in varied sources. The student is expected to:
(D) Read to take action such as to complete forms, make informed recommendations, and write a response. pp. 11, 25, 35, 47, 59, 73, 87, 100–101

(7.9) Reading/vocabulary development. The student acquires an extensive vocabulary through reading and systematic word study. The student is expected to:
(E) Study word meanings systematically such as across curricular content areas and through current events. pp. 3–10, 13–19, 21–24, 27–33, 37–46, 49–50, 52, 54–55, 58, 61–62, 65–68, 70–71, 75–76, 78–83, 85, 89, 92, 95–97

(7.10) Reading/comprehension. The student uses a variety of strategies to comprehend a wide range of texts of increasing levels of difficulty. The student is expected to:
(A) Use his/her own knowledge and experience to comprehend. pp. 3, 8, 11, 25, 35, 59, 101
(C) Monitor his/her own comprehension and make modifications when understanding breaks down such as by rereading a portion aloud, using reference aids, searching for clues, and asking questions. pp. 11, 25, 35, 47, 59, 73, 87, 100–101
(E) Use the text's structure or progression of ideas such as cause and effect or chronology to locate and recall information. pp. 11, 25, 35, 47, 59, 73, 87, 100–101
(F) Determine a text's main (or major) ideas and how those ideas are supported with details. pp. 11, 25, 35, 47, 59, 73, 87, 100–101
(G) Paraphrase and summarize text to recall, inform, or organize ideas. pp. 11, 47, 59, 73, 87, 100
(H) Draw inferences such as conclusions or generalizations and support them with text evidence and experience. pp. 11, 25, 101
(K) Answer different types and levels of questions such as open-ended, literal, and interpretative as well as test-like questions such as multiple choice, true-false, and short answer. pp. 4, 8, 11, 14–15, 25, 35, 47, 59, 73, 87, 100–101
(M) Use study strategies to learn and recall important ideas from texts such as preview, question, reread, and record. pp. 11, 25, 35, 47, 59, 73, 87, 100–101

(7.11) Reading/literary response. The student expresses and supports responses to various types of texts. The student is expected to:
(A) Offer observations, make connections, react, speculate, interpret, and raise questions in response to texts. pp. 3, 11, 13, 25
(B) Interpret text ideas through such varied means as journal writing, discussion, enactment, and media. p. 33
(C) Support responses by referring to relevant aspects of text and his/her own experiences. pp. 4, 11, 25, 59, 101
(D) Connect, compare, and contrast ideas, themes, and issues across text. pp. 33, 65, 83, 94

(7.13) Reading/inquiry/research. The student inquires and conducts research using a variety of sources. The student is expected to:
(C) Use multiple sources, including electronic texts, experts, and print resources, to locate information relevant to research questions. p. 73
(G) Draw conclusions from information gathered from multiple sources. p. 73

(7.15) Writing/purposes. The student writes for a variety of audiences and purposes and in a variety of forms. The student is expected to:
(A) Write to express, discover, record, develop, reflect on ideas, and to problem solve. pp. 11, 25, 33, 35, 59, 101
(B) Write to influence such as to persuade, argue, and request. pp. 25, 87
(C) Write to inform such as to explain, describe, report, and narrate. pp. 11, 25, 35, 47, 59, 73, 87, 100–101
(F) Choose the appropriate form for his/her own purpose for writing such as journals, letters, editorials, reviews, poems, memoirs, narratives, and instructions. p. 33

**(7.16)
Writing/penmanship/capitalization/punctuation/spelling.** The student composes original texts, applying the conventions of written language such as capitalization, punctuation, handwriting, penmanship, and spelling to communicate clearly. The student is expected to:
(A) Write legibly by selecting cursive or manuscript as appropriate. pp. 11, 25, 35, 47, 59, 73, 87, 100–101
(B) Capitalize and punctuate correctly to clarify and enhance meaning such as capitalizing titles, using hyphens, semicolons, colons, possessives, and sentence punctuation. pp. 11, 25, 35, 47, 59, 73, 87, 100–101
(D) Spell frequently misspelled words correctly such as their, they're, and there. pp. 11, 25, 35, 47, 59, 73, 87, 100–101

(7.17) Writing/grammar/usage. The student applies standard grammar and usage to communicate clearly and effectively in writing. The student is expected to:
(A) Write in complete sentences, varying the types such as compound and complex sentences, and use appropriately punctuated independent and dependent clauses. pp. 11, 25, 35, 47, 59, 73, 87, 100–101

For English Language Arts and Reading

Macmillan/McGraw-Hill Your Relationships, Grade 8

English Language Arts and Reading, Grade 8

(8.8) Reading/variety of texts. The student reads widely for different purposes in varied sources. The student is expected to:
(D) Read to take action such as to complete forms, make informed recommendations, and write a response. pp. 11, 25, 35, 47, 59, 73, 87, 100–101

(8.9) Reading/vocabulary development. The student acquires an extensive vocabulary through reading and systematic word study. The student is expected to:

(E) Study word meanings systematically such as across curricular content areas and through current events. pp. 3–10, 13–19, 21–24, 27–33, 37–46, 49–50, 52, 54–55, 58, 61–62, 65–68, 70–71, 75–76, 78–83, 85, 89, 92, 95–97

(8.10) Reading/comprehension. The student uses a variety of strategies to comprehend a wide range of texts of increasing levels of difficulty. The student is expected to:

(A) Use his/her own knowledge and experience to comprehend. pp. 3, 8, 11, 25, 35, 59, 101

(C) Monitor his/her own comprehension and make modifications when understanding breaks down such as by rereading a portion aloud, using reference aids, searching for clues, and asking questions. pp. 11, 25, 35, 47, 59, 73, 87, 100–101

(E) Use the text's structure or progression of ideas such as cause and effect or chronology to locate and recall information. pp. 11, 25, 35, 47, 59, 73, 87, 100–101

(F) Determine a text's main (or major) ideas and how those ideas are supported with details. pp. 11, 25, 35, 47, 59, 73, 87, 100–101

(G) Paraphrase and summarize text to recall, inform, or organize ideas. pp. 11, 47, 59, 73, 87, 100

(H) Draw inferences such as conclusions or generalizations and support them with text evidence and experience. pp. 11, 25, 101

(K) Answer different types and levels of questions such as open-ended, literal, and interpretative as well as test-like questions such as multiple choice, true-false, and short answer. pp. 4, 8, 11, 14–15, 25, 35, 47, 59, 73, 87, 100–101

(M) Use study strategies to learn and recall important ideas from texts such as preview, question, reread, and record. pp. 11, 25, 35, 47, 59, 73, 87, 100–101

(8.11) Reading/literary response. The student expresses and supports responses to various types of texts. The student is expected to:

(A) Offer observations, make connections, react, speculate, interpret, and raise questions in response to texts. pp. 3, 11, 13, 25

(B) Interpret text ideas through such varied means as journal writing, discussion, enactment, and media. p. 33

(C) Support responses by referring to relevant aspects of text and his/her own experiences. pp. 4, 11, 25, 59, 101

(D) Connect, compare, and contrast ideas, themes, and issues across text. pp. 33, 65, 83, 94

(8.13) Reading/inquiry/research. The student inquires and conducts research using a variety of sources. The student is expected to:

(C) Use multiple sources, including electronic texts, experts, and print resources, to locate information relevant to research questions. p. 73

(G) Draw conclusions from information gathered from multiple sources. p. 73

(8.15) Writing/purposes. The student writes for a variety of audiences and purposes and in a variety of forms. The student is expected to:

(A) Write to express, discover, record, develop, reflect on ideas, and to problem solve. pp. 11, 25, 33, 35, 59, 101

(B) Write to influence such as to persuade, argue, and request. pp. 25, 87

(C) Write to inform such as to explain, describe, report, and narrate. pp. 11, 25, 35, 47, 59, 73, 87, 100–101

(F) Choose the appropriate form for his/her own purpose for writing such as journals, letters, editorials, reviews, poems, memoirs, narratives, and instructions. p. 33

(8.16) Writing/penmanship/capitalization/punctuation/spelling. The student composes original texts, applying the conventions of written language such as capitalization, punctuation, handwriting, penmanship, and spelling to communicate clearly. The student is expected to:

(A) Write legibly by selecting cursive or manuscript as appropriate. pp. 11, 25, 35, 47, 59, 73, 87, 100–101

(B) Capitalize and punctuate correctly to clarify and enhance meaning such as capitalizing titles, using hyphens, semicolons, colons, possessives, and sentence punctuation. pp. 11, 25, 35, 47, 59, 73, 87, 100–101

(8.17) Writing/grammar/usage. The student applies standard grammar and usage to communicate clearly and effectively in writing. The student is expected to:

(A) Write in complete sentences, varying the types such as compound and complex sentences, and use appropriately punctuated independent and dependent clauses. pp. 11, 25, 35, 47, 59, 73, 87, 100–101

Texas Assessment of Knowledge and Skills (TAKS)

Macmillan/McGraw-Hill Your Relationships
Correlated with Texas Assessment Knowledge and Skills (TAKS)

For Reading

Macmillan/McGraw-Hill Your Relationships, **Grade 7**
Reading, tested at Grade 7

TAKS Objective 1
The student will demonstrate a basic understanding of culturally diverse written texts.

(7.10) Reading/comprehension. The student uses a variety of strategies to comprehend a wide range of texts of increasing levels of difficulty. The student is expected to:

(F) Determine a text's main (or major) ideas and how those ideas are supported with details. pp. 11, 25, 35, 47, 59, 73, 87, 100–101

(G) Paraphrase and summarize text to recall, inform, or organize ideas. pp. 11, 47, 59, 73, 87, 100

TAKS Objective 3
The student will use a variety of strategies to analyze culturally diverse written texts.

(7.10) Reading/comprehension. The student uses a variety of strategies to comprehend a wide range of texts of increasing levels of difficulty. The student is expected to:

(E) Use the text's structure or progression of ideas such as cause and effect or chronology to locate and recall information. pp. 11, 25, 35, 47, 59, 73, 87, 100–101

TAKS Objective 4
The student will apply critical-thinking skills to analyze culturally diverse written texts.

(7.10) Reading/comprehension. The student uses a variety of strategies to comprehend a wide range of texts of increasing levels of difficulty. The student is expected to:

(H) Draw inferences such as conclusions or generalizations and support them with text evidence [and experience]. pp. 11, 25, 101

(7.11) Reading/literary response. The student expresses and supports responses to various types of texts. The student is expected to:

(C) Support responses by referring to relevant aspects of text [and his/her own experiences]. pp. 4, 11, 25, 59, 101

(D) Connect, compare, and contrast ideas, themes, and issues across text. pp. 33, 65, 83, 94

For Writing

Macmillan/McGraw-Hill Your Relationships, Grade 7

Writing, tested at Grade 7

TAKS Objective 1
The student will, within a given context, produce an effective composition for a specific purpose.

(7.15) Writing/purposes. The student writes for a variety of audiences and purposes and in a variety of forms. The student is expected to:

(A) Write to express, [discover, record,] develop, reflect on ideas, and to problem solve. pp. 11, 25, 33, 35, 59, 101

(B) Write to influence such as to persuade, argue, and request.
pp. 25, 87

(C) Write to inform such as to explain, describe, report, and narrate. pp. 11, 25, 35, 47, 59, 73, 87, 100–101

(7.16)
Writing/penmanship/capitalization/punctuation/spelling. The student composes original texts, applying the conventions of written language such as capitalization, punctuation, handwriting, penmanship, and spelling to communicate clearly. The student is expected to:

(A) Write legibly by selecting cursive or manuscript as appropriate. pp. 11, 25, 35, 47, 59, 73, 87, 100–101

TAKS Objective 2
The student will produce a piece of writing that demonstrates a command of the conventions of spelling, punctuation, grammar, usage, and sentence structure.

(7.16)
Writing/penmanship/capitalization/punctuation/spelling. The student composes original texts, applying the conventions of written language such as capitalization, punctuation, handwriting, penmanship, and spelling to communicate clearly. The student is expected to:

(B) Capitalize and punctuate correctly to clarify and enhance meaning such as capitalizing titles, using hyphens, semi-colons, colons, possessives, and sentence punctuation. pp. 11, 25, 35, 47, 59, 73, 87, 100–101

(D) Spell frequently misspelled words correctly such as their, they're, and there. pp. 11, 25, 35, 47, 59, 73, 87, 100–101

(7.17) Writing/grammar/usage. The student applies standard grammar and usage to communicate clearly and effectively in writing. The student is expected to:

(A) Write in complete sentences, varying the types such as compound and complex sentences, and use appropriately punctuated independent and dependent clauses. pp. 11, 25, 35, 47, 59, 73, 87, 100–101

TAKS Objective 4
The student will recognize correct and effective sentence construction in written text.

(7.17) Writing/grammar/usage. The student applies standard grammar and usage to communicate clearly and effectively in writing. The student is expected to:

(A) Write in complete sentences, varying the types such as compound and complex sentences, and use appropriately punctuated independent and dependent clauses. pp. 11, 25, 35, 47, 59, 73, 87, 100–101

Objective 6
The student will proofread for correct punctuation, capitalization, and spelling in written text.

(7.16) Writing/penmanship/capitalization/punctuation/spelling. The student composes original texts, applying the conventions of written language such as capitalization, punctuation, handwriting, penmanship, and spelling to communicate clearly. The student is expected to:

(B) Capitalize and punctuate correctly to clarify and enhance meaning such as capitalizing titles, using hyphens, semi-colons, colons, possessives, and sentence punctuation. pp. 11, 25, 35, 47, 59, 73, 87, 100–101

(D) Spell frequently misspelled words correctly such as their, they're, and there. pp. 11, 25, 35, 47, 59, 73, 87, 100–101

For Reading

Macmillan/McGraw-Hill Your Relationships, Grade 8

Reading, tested at Grade 8

TAKS Objective 1
The student will demonstrate a basic understanding of culturally diverse written texts.

(8.10) Reading/comprehension. The student comprehends selections using a variety of strategies. The student is expected to:
(F) Determine a text's main (or major) ideas and how those ideas are supported with details.
pp. 11, 25, 35, 47, 59, 73, 87, 100–101

(G) Paraphrase and summarize text to recall, inform, or organize ideas. pp. 11, 47, 59, 73, 87, 100

TAKS Objective 3
The student will use a variety of strategies to analyze culturally written texts.

(8.10) Reading/comprehension. The student comprehends selections using a variety of strategies. The student is expected to:
(E) Use the text's structure or progression of ideas such as cause and effect or chronology to locate and recall information. pp. 11, 25, 35, 47, 59, 73, 87, 100–101

TAKS Objective 4
The student will apply critical-thinking skills to analyze culturally diverse written texts.

(8.10) Reading/comprehension. The student comprehends selections using a variety of strategies. The student is expected to:
(H) Draw inferences such as conclusions or generalizations and support them with text evidence [and experience]. pp. 11, 25, 101

(8.11) Reading/literary response. The student expresses and supports responses to various types of texts. The student is expected to:

(C) Support responses by referring to relevant aspects of text and [his/her own experiences]. pp. 4, 11, 25, 59, 101
(D) Connect, compare, and contrast ideas, themes, and issues across text. pp. 33, 65, 83, 94

CHAPTER 1
Communication

pp. 2–11

Objectives

- Explain ways to express thoughts and feelings honestly and directly.
- Describe how to use I-messages and active listening.
- Describe how to avoid sending mixed messages.
- Discuss ways to resolve conflicts with others.

Health Goals

- Communicate with others in healthful ways.
- Use conflict resolution skills.

Resources

Transparency Book, 6
Assessment Book, Health Behavior Contract, p. vii
Sunburst Videos: *Teen-Adult Conflict: Working It Out; "I'm All That!" Building Self-Esteem*

Sensitivity Caution This chapter discusses communication skills and conflict resolution. Be aware that some students experience conflict regularly or have experience with other people's negative communication strategies. Avoid encouraging students to share personal information with the class.

 QUICK START

Write this statement on the board and discuss its meaning: *"Say what you mean, and mean what you say."* Ask students what the likely consequences are if a person does *not* follow this guideline.

 TEACH

Discuss

Page 4 It has often been said that communication is a "two-way street." Ask students what this means. Discuss why this principle is basic to forming healthful relationships.
Page 5 People with a passive communication style often feel frustrated, and they may either hide their feelings or express them in an inappropriate way. Ask students how they might help a friend who has a passive communication style.

Page 8 People send mixed messages in many different situations. Ask students for additional examples of mixed messages.
Page 9 Present this scenario to the class: Two students are walking down the school hallway arguing loudly. One student pushes the other. Have students use the *Conflict Resolution Skills* to discuss how these students might handle their disagreement in an appropriate manner.

Health Activities

Build Character

Page 6 Honesty Assertive communication is built, in part, on a foundation of being honest. However, a person must also be tactful to avoid hurting someone else's feelings. Have students write several examples of I-messages that are both honest and tactful. Have volunteers share their examples. **Social**

Practice Life Skills

Pages 6–7 Use Communication Skills Have students use the Communication Skills heuristic on page viii to role-play situations such as those described on pages 6 and 7. Encourage students to communicate honestly but also to show sensitivity to the other person's feelings. **Intrapersonal Transparency 6: Use Communication Skills**

 **ASSESS**

Chapter 1 Review p. 11

Use Vocabulary

1. empathy (page 7)
2. active listening (page 8)
3. nonverbal communication (page 8)
4. relationships (page 3)
5. conflict (page 9)

Review Concepts

6. the aggressive communication style (page 5)
7. A person with a passive communication style does not let his or her wants, needs, or opinions be known. The person often withdraws and holds back the truth rather than say what's on his or her mind. (page 5)
8. An assertive communication style expresses thoughts and feelings in an honest and direct manner. It shows respect for the rights of others. (page 5)

9. a specific behavior or event, the effect that the behavior or event has on you, and the feelings that you have as a result (page 6)

10. With an I-message, the speaker focuses on himself or herself: "This is how *I* feel about it." With a you-message, the speaker focuses on the other person: "This is what *you* did," or "What's *your* problem?" (page 6)

11. Ask for more information. Repeat what the other person said using your own words. Summarize the main ideas expressed. Acknowledge the feelings that the person expressed and thank the person for sharing his or her feelings. (page 8)

12. a smile, a high-five, a thumbs-up sign, a frown, putting an arm around another person (page 8)

13. Your words and nonverbal actions convey two different meanings. Your words and tone of voice convey two different meanings. (page 8)

14. poor communication and not treating one another with respect (page 9)

15. Stay calm, talk about the conflict, discuss possible ways to settle the conflict (using the Guidelines for Making Responsible Decisions™), and agree on a responsible way to settle the conflict. (page 9)

Critical Thinking/Problem Solving

16. Responses will vary but should reflect an understanding of the communication styles. (page 5)

17. Responses will vary but should reflect an understanding of I-messages. (page 6)

18. Responses will vary but should reflect an understanding of mixed messages. (page 8)

Practice Life Skills

19. Responses will vary. Plans should show that students have an understanding of the listening skills on page 8.

Health Goals

Review the Health Goals (listed on page T9) with the class. Direct students to write at least one way they can work toward each goal.

CHAPTER 2
Good Character in Relationships

pp. 12–25

Objectives

- Discuss responsible values that make up good character and explain reasons why you need to have good character.
- Explain how to use the *Guidelines for Making Responsible Decisions™*.
- Describe resistance skills to say "no" if you are pressured to choose wrong actions.
- Identify what steps to take to correct wrong actions.
- Tell how to choose friends who have good character.
- Summarize how to work to achieve balanced relationships.
- Explain how to recognize and do something about abusive relationships.

Health Goals

- Develop good character.
- Make responsible decisions.
- Use resistance skills when appropriate.
- Show I am sorry if I do something wrong.
- Take steps to correct wrong actions.
- Develop healthful relationships.
- Recognize harmful relationships.

Resources

Transparency Book, 3
Assessment Book, Health Behavior Contract, p. vii
Sunburst Video: *Student Workshop: Dating Violence and Abuse*

Sensitivity Caution This chapter discusses qualities and behaviors representative of good character. Be sensitive to the fact that some students may recognize flaws in themselves and feel embarrassed or defensive. Stress that a teen's character is still developing and changing and that anyone can become a better person by making a genuine effort.

 QUICK START

Write this phrase on the board: *a good person.* Have students list on a sheet of paper qualities that they associate with being a good person. Ask volunteers to share their lists, and write some of these qualities on the board. Have students discuss how being a good person is reflected in that person's actions.

 TEACH

Discuss

Pages 13–15, 19 Life is filled with choices. Discuss how the choices that a person makes each day reveal the person's character. Point out that even "good" people sometimes make bad choices. Ask how a person can learn from having made a poor choice. Extend the discussion by asking how someone can go about correcting a wrong action that he or she regrets having taken.

Transparency 3: Six Traits of Good Character

Page 16 Write these phrases on the board: *listen to your conscience, let your conscience be your guide, have a clear conscience.* Have students discuss the meaning of these phrases. Ask what role conscience plays in good character.

Page 17 Have volunteers summarize in their own words each step in the process of responsible decision making. Encourage students to provide specific examples.

Page 18 Ask students for examples of positive and negative peer pressure. Then have volunteers summarize how to use resistance skills to oppose negative peer pressure.

Page 20 Have volunteers briefly explain the meaning of each item on the *Good Character Checklist for Choosing Friends* and tell why each item is important.

Pages 21–23 Establishing and maintaining a healthy relationship takes effort. Have students explain what qualities characterize a healthful relationship. Then ask what warning signs might suggest that a relationship is not healthful.

Health Activities

Build Character
Respect It has been said that if you want other people to respect you, you first must respect yourself. Have students explain what they think

this statement means, and then ask them to give examples to illustrate why it is true. Expand the discussion by asking why people of good character are likely to receive the respect of others. **Logical; Intrapersonal**

Practice Life Skills

Use Resistance Skills Have students role-play several situations in which they use the Resistance Skills heuristic on page ix to stand up to peer pressure. After each role play, ask observers to offer constructive suggestions for conveying the "no" message. **Social; Kinesthetic**

 **ASSESS**

Chapter 2 Review p. 25
Use Vocabulary

1. mentor (page 22)
2. integrity (page 15)
3. restitution (page 19)
4. self-control (page 13)
5. citizenship (page 15)

Review Concepts

6. Students should choose their answers from the following: honesty, respect, responsibility, fairness, caring, citizenship, self-discipline, abstinence from sex, determination, courage, integrity. (page 14)

7. to have self-respect; to get along with parents or guardians; to keep the respect of others; to protect the future; to stay out of trouble; to keep a clear conscience (page 16)

8. Is it healthful? Is it safe? Is it legal? Do I show respect for myself and others? Do I follow the guidelines of responsible adults such as my parents or guardian? Do I demonstrate good character? (page 17)

9. Say "no" in a firm voice. Give reasons for saying "no." Be certain your behavior matches your words. Ask an adult for help if you need help. (page 18)

10. Take responsibility for what you have done. Apologize and pledge not to do the wrong action again. Discuss the wrong action with a parent, guardian, or other trusted adult. Accept appropriate punishment. Make restitution. (page 19)

11. Show good character yourself. Listen to the advice responsible adults give you about friends. Use the *Good Character Checklist for Choosing Friends.* (page 20)

12. A control freak gives you no space; is jealous of people you want to be with; allows you no time for your family; pressures you to do things you don't want to do; and is self-centered and not interested in your needs. (page 21)

13. A doormat goes along with whatever you say or do, doesn't set limits, rarely expresses his or her needs, and makes himself or herself available no matter what. (page 21)

14. physical abuse, emotional abuse, sexual abuse, and neglect (page 22)

15. Tell the person to stop the abusive behavior. Tell a responsible adult. Find a mentor. Join a support group. Do not use risk behaviors to cope or get attention. Evaluate your own behavior and stop the cycle of abuse. (page 23)

Critical Thinking/Problem Solving

16. Responses will vary but should reflect an understanding of the signs of good character. (pages 14–15)

17. Responses will vary but should reflect an understanding of choosing friends with good character. (page 20)

Practice Life Skills

18. Responses will vary but should show an understanding of the signs of good character. (pages 14–15)

Health Goals

Review the Health Goals (listed on p. T11) with the class. Direct students to write at least one way they can work toward each goal.

CHAPTER 3
Make Family Life a Priority

pp. 26–35

Objectives

- Describe how to spend quality time with family members.
- Explain why following your family's guidelines is important.
- Examine how to make healthful adjustments to family changes.
- Explain how to recognize and improve difficult family relationships.

Health Goals

- Develop healthful family relationships.
- Follow my family's guidelines.
- Make healthful adjustments to family changes.
- Work to improve difficult family relationships.

Resources

Assessment Book, Health Behavior Contract, p. vii

Sensitivity Caution This chapter discusses families and family relationships. Be sensitive to the fact that some students may have a family situation that is less than ideal. Discuss how a difficult family relationship—like any other relationship—can often be improved through honest communication and patience. Avoid encouraging students to disclose personal information.

 QUICK START

Ask students to write the word *family* on a sheet of paper. Then have them jot down words and phrases that they associate with families and family life. Ask volunteers to describe how a person's relationship with one or more family members can be a source of support or comfort.

 TEACH

Discuss

Page 28 Write the three reasons to spend time with family on the board: *to fulfill your need to belong, to practice taking calculated risks in a safe setting, to learn and practice skills you can use in future relationships.* Have volunteers summarize each reason in their own words and give an example.

Page 29 Ask students how their parents or guardian determine what rules to set. Discuss how adults call upon their knowledge and experience as well as their own family history to establish family guidelines. You might want to extend the discussion by asking the class what consequences or punishment might be appropriate for breaking family guidelines.

Pages 30–32 All families undergo changes. Positive changes can strengthen family relationships. In a way, so can negative changes, because family members must help each other cope. Discuss each of the life events, its possible effects on a family, and strategies for coping.

Page 33 Being a member of a dysfunctional family can be harmful to a person's physical, emotional, and psychological health. Through sincere effort, family members can often improve difficult situations. Discuss what actions might be taken to help a dysfunctional family.

Health Activities

Build Character
Citizenship Family guidelines encourage obeying laws and helping to improve the community— aspects of good citizenship. Ask students to make a pamphlet that explains how the efforts of one family can benefit other families, or even an entire community. **Intrapersonal; Logical**

Practice Life Skills
Resolve Conflicts Have students role-play situations in which they use the skill heuristic for Resolving Conflicts on page ix to work out a disagreement between family members. Ask observers to offer constructive suggestions after each role play. **Kinesthetic**

③ ASSESS

Chapter 3 Review p. 35

Use Vocabulary

1. calculated risk (page 28)
2. unnecessary risk (page 28)
3. dysfunctional family (page 33)
4. marital separation (page 30)
5. addiction (page 33)

Review Concepts

6. Peers do not have the experience and wisdom of adults. Peers are not responsible for you. They do not have to be concerned about your future. They may not always have your long-term best interests at heart. (page 28)

7. Family members can help you see the difference between unnecessary and calculated risks. They can support you when you take a calculated risk and do not get what you wanted. (page 28)

8. They treat you with affection and they take responsible actions concerning your welfare. (page 29)

9. to protect your health and safety, to follow rules and laws, to show respect for yourself and others, to show good character (page 29)

10. birth or adoption of a family member; separation, divorce, or remarriage of parents; illness or injury that affects a family member; military service, fulfilling a work assignment away from home, going away to attend college; the death of a family member (pages 30–31)

11. Get plenty of rest and sleep; eat a balanced diet of healthful foods; get plenty of exercise; have a plan to manage stress. (page 32)

12. Share feelings with family members. Write about your feelings in a notebook or a letter to yourself. (page 32)

13. Ask questions to be sure of what is expected of you. Get details about how your routine might change. Offer to help other family members to change their routines. Ask for help if you feel overwhelmed. (page 32)

14. drug dependence, other addictions, abuse, violence, abandonment (page 33)

15. Keep notes of any difficult situations. Talk to a responsible adult family member. Participate in a recovery program. (page 33)

Critical Thinking/Problem Solving

16. The family fulfills your need to belong. Family members provide love, support, and encouragement, and help you learn to deal with difficult situations. They teach you things you cannot readily learn from your peers. You learn to practice skills you can use in future relationships. Family relationships also prepare you for other relationships. (page 28)

17. Worry about the person will be an ongoing stress. There will be new family responsibilities. Teens may have to help out more and change their habits. The grandparent's condition may require changes in the household schedule and activities. There may be some loss of income for family members and large medical bills. Family members may have to put off planned purchases. If the grandparent has to go to the hospital, time that would be spent in other ways must then be spent visiting the grandparent at the hospital. (pages 30–31)

Practice Life Skills

18. Responses will vary but should reflect an understanding of calculated risks and unnecessary risks. (page 28)

Health Goals

Review the Health Goals (listed on p. T13) with the class. Direct students to write at least one way they can work toward each goal.

CHAPTER 4
Body Changes

pp. 36–47

Objectives

- Explain how differences in growth patterns among adolescents, such as onset of puberty, may affect personal health.
- Examine physical and emotional development during adolescence.
- Describe habits that protect male reproductive health.
- Describe habits that protect female reproductive health.
- Explain what happens during the menstrual cycle.

Health Goals

- Recognize habits that protect female reproductive health.
- Recognize habits that protect male reproductive health.

Resources

Transparency Book, 17, 45

Assessment Book, Responsible Decision Making Model™, p. xii, and Health Behavior Contract, p. vii

Sensitivity Caution This chapter discusses puberty and the male and female reproductive systems. Be sensitive to students who may have delayed onset of puberty or who are noticeably mature. Although some students may feel embarrassed to talk about puberty and reproduction, help them to understand that these topics are a normal part of human development. Encourage students to learn about the material in a mature manner.

① QUICK START

Have each student write the words *childhood* and *adolescence* on a piece of paper. Then have them list a few words or phrases that come to mind when they think of these two stages in life. Ask volunteers to describe how these life stages are different.

② TEACH

Discuss

Pages 38–39 Write this statement on the board: *Every teen's body changes as he or she moves from childhood toward adulthood. However, these changes happen at different times and at different rates for each individual.* Discuss how such differences may affect teens and their relationships.

Interpret the Illustration

Page 40 Have students locate each part of the male reproductive system in the illustration, summarize its function, and explain how it is related to other parts.
Transparency 17: The Male and Female Reproductive Systems

Discuss

Pages 41, 44–45 Both men and women can practice habits to protect their reproductive health. Discuss with students how these habits are the same for both genders and how they are different. Use a Venn diagram to enhance the discussion.
Transparency 45: Venn Diagram

Interpret the Illustrations

Page 42 Have students describe the three functions of the female reproductive system and explain how each part of the system relates to these functions.
Transparency 17: The Male and Female Reproductive Systems

Page 43 Refer students to the diagram of the menstrual cycle. Explain that, although the cycle usually lasts 28 days, the normal range is between 21 and 35 days. Women will probably have cycles of many different lengths during their reproductive years.

Health Activities

Practice Life Skills

Make Responsible Decisions Pose the following situation to students: Your boyfriend or girlfriend is pressuring you to engage in sexual activity, but you want to practice abstinence. Have students use the skill heuristic for Making Responsible Decisions on page ix when discussing how to handle this situation in a responsible way. **Intrapersonal**

Be a Health Advocate Have students use the skill heuristic for Health Advocacy on page ix to make a poster describing dos and don'ts to protect the reproductive system. Posters should convey their message through a creative combination of text and images. **Kinesthetic**

③ ASSESS

Chapter 4 Review p. 47

Use Vocabulary

1. *Cowper's glands:* Two small glands that secrete a clear fluid into the urethra (page 40)

2. *epididymis:* A structure on the top of the testes where sperm mature (page 40)

3. *prostate gland:* A gland that produces fluid that helps keep sperm alive (page 40)

4. *scrotum:* A saclike pouch that holds the testes and helps regulate their temperature (page 40)

5. *seminal vesicles:* Two small glands that secrete a fluid rich in sugar that nourishes and helps sperm move (page 40)

6. *testes:* Two glands that produce testosterone and sperm, the male reproductive cells (page 40)

7. *urethra:* A narrow tube through which urine and semen pass out of the body (page 40)

8. *vas deferens:* One of two long, thin tubes that act as passageways for sperm and a place for sperm storage (page 40)

9. *cervix:* The lower part of the uterus that connects to the vagina (page 42)

10. *vagina:* A muscular tube that connects the uterus with the outside of the body. The vagina serves as the birth canal and the passageway for the menstrual flow. (page 42)

11. *fallopian tube:* A four-inch (ten centimeter)–long tube through which ova move from an ovary to the uterus. A female has two fallopian tubes— one near each ovary. (page 42)

12. *ovaries:* Two glands that produce estrogen and ova, the female reproductive cells. Ova are also called eggs. One egg is called an ovum. (page 42)

13. *uterus:* A muscular organ that receives and supports a fertilized ovum during pregnancy (page 42)

Review Concepts

14. Use the correct terms to refer to them; practice specific healthful behaviors. (page 37)

15. male: testosterone; female: estrogen (page 38)

16. Mood swings are caused by changing hormone levels. (page 38)

17. increase in height; increase in perspiration; growth of underarm hair and pubic hair; growth of facial hair; broadening of shoulders; deepening of voice; increase in the size of reproductive organs; increase in muscle mass; formation of mature sperm (page 39)

18. increase in height; increase in perspiration; growth of underarm hair and pubic hair; increase in breast size; widening of hips; increase in size of reproductive organs; beginning of menstruation; formation of mature ova (page 39)

19. seminal vesicles, prostate gland, Cowper's glands, epididymis, scrotum, testes, urethra, penis, vas deferens (page 40)

20. Practice abstinence from sex until marriage. Do not smoke. Perform a TSE. Bathe or shower daily. Have regular medical checkups. Get medical attention for signs of infection. Wear an athletic supporter and protective cup for sports. (page 41)

21. the ovaries, uterus, fallopian tubes, cervix, and vagina (page 42)

22. See page 43 for the complete answer.

23. Practice abstinence from sex until marriage. Do not smoke. Change pads, panty shields, and tampons often. Get prompt medical attention for symptoms of toxic shock syndrome. Keep track of the menstrual cycle on a calendar. Limit caffeine and sodium and get plenty of exercise. Perform a BSE each month. Have regular medical checkups. Get medical attention for signs of infections or missed periods. (page 44)

Critical Thinking/Problem Solving

24. Teens who have a positive body image are comfortable with the way they look, which is essential for good health and relationships. (page 38)

25. Males: Smoking harms the arteries that bring blood to the penis, which can result in impotence. Smoking changes the number, shape, and quality of a male's sperm. Females: Smoking harms the arteries that bring blood to a female's reproductive organs. (pages 41–42)

Practice Life Skills

26. Practicing abstinence reduces the risk of infection with HIV and sexually transmitted diseases, which can cause a person to be infertile, or incapable of producing offspring.

Health Goals

Review the Health Goals (listed on p. T15) with the class. Direct students to write at least one way they can work toward each goal.

CHAPTER 5
Choose Abstinence from Sex

pp. 48–59

Objectives

- Discuss why abstinence from sex is the expected standard for you and reasons to practice abstinence from sex.
- Explain the rules and responsibilities of dating.
- Apply the Guidelines for Expressing Affection.
- Explain why it is risky to drink alcohol or use other drugs.
- Describe what can happen if you are slipped a drug and how to reduce the risk of being slipped a drug.
- Show how to choose entertainment that promotes family values.
- Identify resistance skills you can use if you are pressured to be sexually active.
- List steps that teens who have been sexually active can take to change their behavior.

Health Goals

- Practice abstinence from sex until marriage.
- Set limits for expressing affection.
- Choose a drug-free lifestyle to support my decision to practice abstinence.
- Choose entertainment to support my decision to practice abstinence.
- Use resistance skills if I am pressured to be sexually active.

Resources

Transparency Book, 44
Assessment Book, Health Behavior Contract, p. vii
Sunburst Videos: *The Fourth "R": Responsibility; Student Workshop: Dating Violence and Abuse*

Sensitivity Caution This chapter deals with sexuality and drugs. Be aware that some students may be sexually active or may have experimented with drugs. Some may have been born to teen parents or have teen parents in the family. Try to avoid a judgmental tone, and try not to encourage personal anecdotes.

 QUICK START

Draw a word web on the board. Write the word *Risks* in the center circle. In three smaller circles connected to the main circle, write the words *Sexual Activity, Alcohol, Drugs.* Ask students to interpret the web's meaning. Then discuss how their interpretation may differ from that of their parents or guardians.
Transparency 44: Venn Diagram

 TEACH

Discuss
Page 50 Group dating is a way to get to know members of the opposite sex without the pressure of individual dating. Ask students which of the group activities listed on page 50 they would most enjoy. Then invite them to add their own suggestions.
Page 51 Ask students why each of the questions listed under the heading "The Person You Are Dating" is important. Encourage them to list the qualities they would look for in a date.
Page 52 Ask students to relate positive and healthful ways of showing affection. Ask them why they believe that affection is important.
Page 54 It is important for teens to know how impaired judgment might cause them to put their health and safety at risk. Review the numbered list at the bottom of the page with students. Stress the importance of a person being in control of making his or her decisions.
Page 55 Have students form a class roundtable for discussion. Invite them to list their favorite TV programs. Then evaluate each show on the list, asking students to vote on whether the program does or does not promote family values.
Page 57 One of life's basic truths is that all actions have consequences. Discuss with students the possible consequences of *not* practicing abstinence.

Health Activities
Practice Life Skills
Pages 56–57 Practice Healthful Behaviors Using the skill heuristic for Practicing Healthful Behaviors on page viii, have the class brainstorm as many responses as they can that a teen could give to a boyfriend or girlfriend who says, "Abstinence is silly. Why should we wait?" Write students' responses on the board. Discuss which ones are the strongest. **Kinesthetic**

Build Character

Page 53 Responsibility A sign of maturity is learning to take responsibility for one's own actions. Have students make a poster illustrating what they think this means. Have students show how teens must accept more responsibility as they get older. **Intrapersonal**

 ASSESS

Chapter 5 Review p. 59

Use Vocabulary

1. sexual feelings (page 52)
2. rape (page 54)
3. affection (page 52)
4. abstinence from sex (page 49)
5. family values (page 55)

Review Concepts

6. Abstinence from sex is healthful, safe, follows rules and laws, shows respect for self and others, follows family guidelines, and shows good character. (page 53)
7. See page 52 for the complete answer.
8. See page 54 for the complete answer.
9. You may pass out and become a victim of rape without being aware of it. (page 54)
10. See page 54 for the complete answer.
11. Ideas and images from entertainment can be powerful influences that are hard to shake. They may lead to faulty thinking that undermines a decision to practice abstinence. (page 55)

12. Entertainment that promotes family values is approved for the age group; is approved by parents or guardian; does not show drug use as acceptable behavior; does not show sex outside of marriage as acceptable behavior; does not show violence or sexual assault as acceptable behavior. (page 55)
13. Say "no" in a firm voice; give reasons for practicing abstinence; repeat your reasons for practicing abstinence; don't send a mixed message; avoid situations in which there will be pressure to be sexually active; break off a relationship when someone does not respect your limits; influence others to practice abstinence. (page 56)
14. See page 56 for the complete answer.
15. See page 57 for the complete answer.

Critical Thinking/Problem Solving

16. See page 50 for the complete answer.
17. Responses will vary. Most parents support limits that do not encourage or lead to sexual activity. (page 52)
18. Leave the party, call them, and don't drink. (page 51)

Practice Life Skills

19. Answers will vary but should reflect an understanding of what influences health.

Health Goals

Review the Health Goals (listed on p. T17) with the class. Direct students to write at least one way they can work toward each goal.

CHAPTER 6
Prevent Teen Marriage, Pregnancy, and Parenthood

pp. 60–73

Objectives

- Examine the benefits of a monogamous traditional marriage.
- Identify reasons why teen marriage and parenthood are risky.
- Discuss reasons why you should be a married adult before you become a parent.
- Explain ways in which the behavior of mothers-to-be and fathers-to-be can affect the health of their baby.
- Describe how an embryo and a fetus develop.
- Explain what happens during childbirth.
- Describe how parents bond with their baby.

Health Goals

- Practice abstinence from sex to prevent teen marriage, pregnancy, and parenthood.
- Wait to get married until I am an adult, have completed my education, and am able to handle the responsibilities of marriage.
- Wait until I am a married adult to become a parent.

Resources

Transparency Book, 42, 45
Assessment Book, Health Behavior Contract, p. vii

Sensitivity Caution This chapter discusses teen marriage and pregnancy. Be aware that some students may have parents, guardians, or other family members who married and/or had children at a very young age. Try to maintain a factual, nonjudgmental tone in classroom discussions. Avoid encouraging students to share personal information that might cause embarrassment.

QUICK START

Have volunteers suggest favorite after-school and weekend activities. List five or six student suggestions on the board. Then ask students to imagine that they are teen parents, with a newborn baby to care for. Ask how being a parent would affect their ability to take part in the activities listed.

TEACH

Discuss
Page 62 In some ways, marriage is like other relationships, but in other ways, it is unique. Discuss with students what makes the marriage relationship special. You may want to use a Venn diagram to enhance the discussion. In the context of the discussion, ask why it is important for marriage partners to be able to answer "yes" to the questions on page 62.
Transparency 45: Venn Diagram

Pages 63–65 Create a three-column chart on the board. Title the chart *RISKS*, and use these headings: *Teen Marriage, Teen Parenthood, Teen Pregnancy.* Complete the chart as students summarize the risks in their own words.
Transparency 42: Three-Column Chart

Pages 68–69 Draw a chart on the board dividing pregnancy into first, second, and third trimesters. Have students explain what occurs during each trimester. Write key words on the board under each trimester.
Transparency 42: Three-Column Chart

Interpret the Illustration
Page 70 Have students refer to the drawings as they summarize what happens during childbirth.

Discuss
Page 71 Call students' attention to the first sentence: *Responsible parents put raising their children first in their lives.* Ask students to explain why this is an important statement and to describe what it means to be a "responsible" parent.

Health Activities

Practice Life Skills
Set Health Goals Present students with this scenario: Two of your friends are telling you that practicing abstinence is dumb, but you want to make practicing abstinence a health goal. Use the

skill heuristic for Setting Health Goals on page ix to write a letter to your friends explaining your reasons for making abstinence a health goal. **Logical; Social**

Pages 66–67 Analyze What Influences Your Health Both a male's and a female's health habits can affect a baby they may decide to have in the future. Using the skill heuristic for Analyzing Influences on page viii, review the behaviors discussed on these two pages. List three healthful behaviors students should practice now and in the future. **Intrapersonal**

 **ASSESS**

Chapter 6 Review p. 73

Use Vocabulary

1. infertile (page 66)
2. commitment (page 61)
3. pregnancy (page 67)
4. conception (page 67)
5. bonding (page 61)

Review Concepts

6. Possible answers: A monogamous traditional marriage protects the marriage commitment, preserves the tradition of marriage, helps prevent divorce, provides emotional security and trust, helps protect marriage partners from infections with HIV and other STDs, and provides secure family life for children of the marriage. (page 62)

7. See page 63 for the complete answer.

8. Married adults are better able to provide a stable home life for children, more likely to have the financial resources necessary to raise a child, and more mature and capable of meeting the responsibilities of parenthood. (page 64)

9. Babies born to teen parents often do not receive adequate nourishment, often do not receive adequate prenatal care, risk being born prematurely and having a low birth weight, are more likely to be abused or neglected by their parents, and are less likely to have adequate medical and dental care as children. (page 65)

10. See page 65 for the complete answer.

11. Teen fathers may have to pay child support and be financially stressed, are more likely to drop out of school because they must get a job, are less likely to meet their career goals, and are more likely to neglect or abuse their children. (page 65)

12. See page 66 for the complete answer.

13. See page 67 for the complete answer.

14. See page 70 for the complete answer.

15. soft touches; gently spoken words; smiles; providing quality care, such as feeding and changing diapers gently; careful holding; hugging; soft rocking (page 71)

Critical Thinking/Problem Solving

16. **(a)** Responses may vary, but students should recognize that the statement is not true. Engaging in sexual activity just once *can* result in pregnancy.

    (b) Responses may vary, but the statement is not likely true. Most teen fathers do not marry the mother of their child.

    (c) Responses may vary, but the "fun" is likely to be outweighed by the loss of friends and activities, and the sheer work involved in raising a child.

    (d) Responses may vary, but students should understand that males are just as responsible morally, legally, and financially for their actions as females.

    (e) Responses may vary, but the attention is likely to be short lived as others go on with their lives and teen parents must assume their childcare responsibilities.

17. See page 69 for the complete answer.

Practice Life Skills

18. Responses will vary but should reflect knowledge about accessing health information, products, and services. (page 71)

Health Goals

Review the Health Goals (listed on p. T19) with the class. Direct students to write at least one way they can work toward each goal.

CHAPTER 7
Choose Abstinence to Prevent Sexually Transmitted Diseases

pp. 74–87

Objectives

- Identify the cause, method of transmission, symptoms, complications, diagnosis, and treatment for the following STDs: chlamydia, gonorrhea, syphilis, nongonococcal urethritis, genital herpes, genital warts, viral hepatitis, trichomoniasis, and pubic lice.

- Describe ways to reduce the risk of becoming infected with STDs.

- Explain why abstinence from sexual activity is the only method that is 100 percent effective in preventing the sexual transmission of STDs.

Health Goal

- Practice abstinence to reduce my risk of infection with STDs.

Resources

Transparency Book, 44
Assessment Book, Health Behavior Contract, page vii
Sunburst Video: *Sexually Transmitted Infections: What You Should Know*

Sensitivity Caution This chapter discusses sexually transmitted diseases (STDs). Be sensitive to the fact that some students may feel uncomfortable or embarrassed discussing this material. Encourage students to recognize the seriousness of the chapter content and to approach the material in a mature manner.

① QUICK START

Write the following statements on the board, or read them aloud to students. Have the class vote as to whether each statement is true or false.

- *Sexually transmitted diseases can easily be cured with antibiotics.*

- *You can always tell when someone has an STD.*

- *The chances of getting an STD are small.*

Students may be surprised to learn that all three statements are false. Explain that people have many misconceptions about STDs.

② TEACH

Discuss

Pages 76–77 Write on the board the vocabulary words that appear on these pages. You may want to display one or more word webs to show how the terms are linked. Write the word *pathogen* (germ). As you lead a discussion of the facts about sexually transmitted diseases, have students explain the meaning of each term.
Transparency 44: Word Web

Discuss

Pages 78–82 Review the information on STDs with the class. Then have students assess each other's knowledge of STD facts. Have each student write 10 questions about STDs on a sheet of paper. The questions should cover the material on pages 78–82. Students should write the answers to their questions on a separate sheet of paper. Have students trade papers and answer the questions. Then have the student who wrote the questions grade the paper.
Page 83 Have students explain in their own words the flaw in each of the four statements.
Pages 84–85 Lead a discussion of the nine points presented. Have students explain how self-control and personal responsibility are the keys to all nine.

Health Activities

Build Character

Fairness Fairness—showing equal courtesy and respect to everyone—is a sign of good character. Ask students why knowing ways to reduce the risk of becoming infected with STDs shows fairness to themselves, their families, and their friends.

Practice Life Skills

Access Valid Health Information, Products, and Services Teens often want to know more about sexually transmitted diseases but feel uncertain about where to turn and embarrassed to ask. Using the heuristic skill for Accessing Valid Health Information on page viii, have students design a one-page newsletter giving sources of information, such as the Internet and one's family physician. Stress that learning the facts is far wiser than getting half-truths from peers.

③ ASSESS

Use Vocabulary

1. treatment (page 76)
2. pelvic inflammatory disease (page 76)
3. sexually transmitted disease (STD) (page 75)
4. gonorrhea (page 78)
5. genital herpes (page 80)

Review Concepts

6. See page 78 for the complete answer.
7. See page 78 for the complete answer.
8. See page 79 for the complete answer.
9. See page 80 for the complete answer.
10. See page 80 for the complete answer.
11. See page 81 for the complete answer.
12. See page 82 for the complete answer.
13. See page 83 for the complete answer.
14. Abstain from sex until marriage, change behavior if sexually active, have a monogamous marriage, choose a drug-free lifestyle, avoid the use of injection drugs, change your behavior if you use drugs, avoid sharing needles for tattoos or body piercings, follow universal precautions, and choose other responsible behaviors. (page 85)
15. A teen who has sex just once can't get an STD. A teen would know if a partner was infected with an STD. A teen who has been sexually active and does not have symptoms does not need to be examined and/or tested for STDs. A teen who has symptoms of an STD can't talk to his or her parents or guardian. (page 84)

Critical Thinking/Problem Solving

16. Sometimes people do not show symptoms but still are infected by the STD and risk later complications. (page 85)
17. Pathogens that cause one or more STDs might be transmitted by having contact with infected blood. (page 85)

Practice Life Skills

18. Responses will vary. Essays should include the nine behaviors on page 85.

Health Goal

Review the Health Goal (listed on p. T21) with the class. Direct students to write at least one way they can work toward this goal.

CHAPTER 8
Choose Abstinence to Reduce the Risk of HIV and AIDS

pp. 88–101

Objectives

- Examine ways in which HIV *is* and *is not* spread.
- Explain why practicing abstinence protects you from HIV infection.
- Explain why saying "no" to sharing needles to make tattoos or to pierce your body protects you from HIV infection.
- Describe universal precautions to follow to protect yourself from HIV infection.
- Describe tests used to determine HIV status.
- Explain how HIV infection progresses to AIDS.
- Discuss treatments for HIV and AIDS.
- Examine ways in which HIV and AIDS threaten society.
- Identify resistance skills you can use if you are pressured to choose risk behaviors for HIV infection.

Health Goal

- Practice abstinence to reduce my risk of HIV infection and AIDS.

Resources

Transparency Book, 37, 41
Assessment Book, Health Behavior Contract, p. vii
Sunburst Video: *AIDS: One Teenager's Story*

Sensitivity Caution This chapter discusses HIV and AIDS and the high-risk behaviors associated with them. Be sensitive to the fact that some students may feel uncomfortable discussing this topic. Also be aware that some students may have acquaintances or relatives who are HIV positive. Avoid encouraging students to disclose personal information.

 QUICK START

Write the words *HIV* and *AIDS* on the board. Have students summarize in their own words how HIV and AIDS are related and how they are different. Explain that there are many misunderstandings about these diseases. It is important that students know that the two are not synonymous, but that HIV is the pathogen that causes AIDS.

 TEACH

Discuss
Page 90 Make a two-column chart on the board. Title the chart *How Is HIV Spread?* and use these column headings: *Yes, No.* Work with students to fill in the chart.
Transparency 41: Two-Column Chart

Pages 91–93 Write these phrases on the board: *intimate sexual contact, drug use, sharing needles.* Have volunteers explain why, in the context of HIV and AIDS, each is dangerous and potentially self-destructive.
Page 94 Review with students the universal precautions. Stress that, whenever possible, first aid should be administered by a trained professional.
Page 95 Write on the board the vocabulary words that appear on this page. Ask volunteers to explain the meaning of each term as you lead a discussion of HIV testing.

Interpret the Illustration
Page 96 Remind students that T cells are cells that fight infection in the body. Have students review the definitions of HIV and AIDS and then describe how HIV infection progresses to AIDS.
Transparency 37: How HIV Attacks the Immune System

Discuss
Page 97 Review NRTIs and NNRTIs and how they work differently from protease inhibitors in the treatment of HIV/AIDS. Tell students that the combination of drugs used for treatment, *HAART*, is sometimes called a "cocktail."
Page 98 Lead a discussion of the seven points presented. Stress the importance of taking personal responsibility for one's actions.

Health Activities

Build Character

Caring Caring people feel empathy for those who are in pain or distress and try to help them if they can. Ask students what actions might be taken to help people who are HIV positive or who have AIDS, either in this country or elsewhere in the world. Extend the discussion by examining the effects of AIDS on the family members of infected people. **Intrapersonal; Logical**

Practice Life Skills

Manage Stress People who are infected with HIV/AIDS are under a great deal of stress trying to manage their health. Ask students to find an article about people who are helping those who have HIV/AIDS and share it with the class. Using the skill heuristic for Managing Stress on page viii, ask students to decide how these people are helping to manage the stress of the person with HIV/AIDS. **Social**

 **ASSESS**

Chapter 8 Review p. 100

Use Vocabulary

1. human immunodeficiency virus (HIV) (page 89)
2. opportunistic infections (page 96)
3. Kaposi's sarcoma (page 96)
4. HIV negative (page 95)
5. AIDS dementia (page 96)

Review Concepts

6. See page 90 for the complete answer.
7. See page 90 for the complete answer.
8. A male infected with HIV has the virus in his semen. A female infected has the HIV virus in her vaginal secretions. A person can become infected with HIV if he or she has intimate sexual contact with an HIV-infected partner. (page 91)
9. You could become infected with HIV if you share a needle, syringe, or injection equipment that has been used by a person who is infected with HIV. Saying "no" to this behavior protects you from HIV infection. (page 92)
10. See page 92 for the complete answer.
11. See page 93 for the complete answer.
12. See page 94 for the complete answer.
13. If a person is infected with HIV, the person's immune system will begin to make HIV antibodies to try to fight the virus. HIV testing checks to see whether there are HIV antibodies present. If there are, the person is HIV positive. (page 95)
14. See page 96 for the complete answer.
15. See page 98 for the complete answer.

Critical Thinking/Problem Solving

16. **(a)** Not true. A person who is infected with HIV can appear healthy. (page 91)
    (b) Not true. Any person who engages in risk behaviors for HIV can become infected.
    (c) HIV can be transmitted by contact with infected blood. Universal precautions reduce the risk. (page 94)
    (d) Not true. HIV antibodies may not show up in testing for up to six months or more. During that time, test results may be negative though the person is infected with the virus and can transmit it to others. (page 95)
    (e) Not true. A person with AIDS can worsen his or her own health by practicing harmful behaviors, and can transmit the HIV virus to others.
    (f) AIDS has not been shown to be transmitted by donating blood. (page 90)
    (g) Not true. The needle used to make a tattoo might have been used to make a tattoo on someone else, perhaps a person who was infected with HIV. (page 93)
17. The rule limits the risk of transmission of body fluid from such a cut to an open sore or cut on another player. This lessens the risk of HIV infection. (page 94)
18. Answers may vary. Possible answers include: early detection of disease offers the best possibility of treatment; a teen may have engaged in previous sexual activity that might have exposed him or her to HIV or other STDs; a teen may not have been fully honest with his or her partner about previous sexual activity. (page 91)

Practice Life Skills

19. Responses will vary but should show an understanding of the risk behaviors for HIV infection. (pages 92–93)

Health Goal

Review the Health Goal (listed on p. T23) with the class. Direct students to write at least one way they can work toward this goal.

Your Relationships

Choosing Abstinence and Good Character

Linda Meeks
The Ohio State University

Philip Heit
The Ohio State University

Macmillan
McGraw-Hill

About the Authors

Professor Linda Meeks and Dr. Philip Heit

Linda Meeks and Philip Heit are emeritus professors of Health Education in the College of Education at The Ohio State University. As faculty members, Linda and Philip held joint appointments in Health Education in the College of Education and in Allied Medicine in the College of Medicine. Linda and Philip are America's most widely published health education co-authors. They have collaborated for more than 25 years, co-authoring more than 300 health books that are used by millions of students from preschool through college. They are co-authors of an organized, sequential K–12 health education program, *Health and Wellness,* available from Macmillan/McGraw-Hill. Together, they have helped state departments of education as well as thousands of school districts develop comprehensive school health education curricula. Their books and curricula are used throughout the United States, as well as in Canada, Japan, Mexico, England, Puerto Rico, Spain, Egypt, Jordan, Saudi Arabia, Bermuda, and the Virgin Islands. Linda and Philip train professors as well as educators in state departments of education and school districts. Their book *Comprehensive School Health Education: Totally Awesome® Strategies for Teaching Health* is the most widely used book for teacher training in colleges, universities, state departments of education, and school districts. Thousands of teachers around the world have participated in their *Totally Awesome® Teacher Training Workshops*. Linda and Philip have been the keynote speakers for many teacher institutes and wellness conferences. They are personally and professionally committed to the health and well-being of youth.

The McGraw·Hill Companies

Macmillan
McGraw-Hill

Published by Macmillan/McGraw-Hill, of McGraw-Hill Education, a division of The McGraw-Hill Companies, Inc., Two Penn Plaza, New York, New York 10121.

Printed in the United States of America
1 2 3 4 5 6 7 8 9 079 09 08 07 06 05 04

Contributors

Celan Alo, M.D., MPH
Medical Epidemiologist
Bureau of Chronic Diseases and Tobacco
  Prevention
Texas Department of Education
Austin, Texas

Danny Ballard, Ed.D.
Associate Professor, Health
Texas A&M University
College of Education
College Station, Texas

Lucille Villegas Barrera, M.ED.
Elementary Science Specialist
Houston Independent School District
Houston, Texas

Gus T. Dalis, Ed.D.
Consultant of Health Education
Torrance, California

Alisa Evans-Debnam, MPH
Dean of Health Programs
Fayetteville Technical Community College
Fayetteville, North Carolina

Susan C. Giarratano-Russell, MSPH, Ed.D., CHES
Health Education, Evaluation and Media
  Consultant
National Center for Chronic Disease
  Prevention and Health Promotion
Centers for Disease Control and Prevention
Glendale, California

Donna Lloyd-Kolkin, Ph.D.
Principal Associate
Public Health Applications and Research
Abt Associates, Inc.
Bethesda, Maryland

Mulugheta Teferi, M.A.
Principal
Gateway Middle School
Center for Math, Science and
  Technology
St. Louis, Missouri

Roberto P. Treviño, M.D.
Director, Social and Health
  Research Center
Bienestar School-Based Diabetes
  Prevention Program
San Antonio, Texas

Dinah Zike, M.Ed.
Dinah Might Adventures LP
San Antonio, Texas

Content Reviewers

Mark Anderson
Supervisor, Health Physical
  Education
Cobb County Public Schools
Marietta, Georgia

Ken Ascoli
Assistant Principal
Our Lady of Fatima High
  School
Warren, Rhode Island

Jane Beougher, Ph.D.
Professor Emeritus of Health
  Education, Physical
  Education, and Education
Capital University
Westerville, Ohio

Lillie Burns
HIV/AIDS Prevention
  Education
Education Program
  Coordinator
Louisiana Department of
  Education
Baton Rouge, Louisiana

Jill English, Ph.D., CHES
Professor
Soka University
Aliso Viejo, California

Elizabeth Gallun, M.A.
Specialist, Comprehensive
  Health Education
Maryland State Department
  of Education
Baltimore, Maryland

Brenda Garza
Health Communications
  Specialist
Centers for Disease Control
  and Prevention
Atlanta, Georgia

Sheryl Gotts, M.S.
Consultant
Retired from Milwaukee
  Schools
Milwaukee, Wisconsin

Diane Hensley
Envision Training System
Hewitt, Texas

Russell Henke, M.Ed.
Coordinator of Health
Montgomery County Public
  Schools
Rockville, Maryland

Kathy Kent
Health and Physical
  Education Teacher
Simpsonville Elementary
  School at Morton Place
Simpsonville, South Carolina

Bill Moser, M.S.
Program Specialist for
  Health and Character
  Education
Winston-Salem Forsyth City
  Schools
Winston-Salem, North
  Carolina

Debra Ogden
Curriculum Coordinator
District School Board of
  Collier County
Naples, Florida

Thurman Robins
Chair/Professor
Health and Kinesiology
  Department
Texas Southern University
Houston, Texas

Sherman Sowby, Ph.D., CHES
Professor
Department of Health Science
California State University
  at Fresno
Fresno, California

Deitra Wengert, Ph.D., CHES
Professor
Department of Health
  Science
Towson University
Towson, Maryland

Susan Wooley-Goekler, Ph.D., CHES
Adjunct Faculty
Kent State University
Kent, Ohio

Medical Reviewers

Celan Alo, M.D., MPH
Medical Epidemiologist
Bureau of Chronic Diseases
  and Tobacco Prevention
Texas Department of
  Education
Austin, Texas

Donna Bacchi, M.D., MPH
Associate Professor of
  Pediatrics
Director, Division of
  Community Pediatrics
Texas Tech University
Health Science Center
Lubbock, Texas

Olga Dominguez Satterwhite, R.D., L.D.
Registered Dietitian and
  Diabetes Educator
Baylor College of Medicine
Houston, Texas

Roberto P. Treviño, M.D.
Director, Social and Health
  Research Center
Bienestar School-Based
  Diabetes Prevention
  Program
San Antonio, Texas

Your Relationships
Choosing Abstinence and Good Character

The Ten Life Skills

Throughout this course you will learn ten life skills. These skills will help you improve and maintain your health throughout your life. They will also help you influence the health status of others. By making a commitment to practice these life skills, you can achieve physical, mental and emotional, and family and social health. Each life skill involves four basic steps.

Analyze what influences your health.

1. Identify people and things that might influence you.
2. Evaluate how the influence might affect your health and decisions.
3. Choose positive influences on health.
4. Protect yourself from negative influences on health.

Practice healthful behaviors.

1. Learn about a healthful behavior.
2. Practice the healthful behavior in the correct way.
3. Ask for help if you need it.
4. Make the healthful behavior a habit.

Manage stress.

1. Know the signs of stress.
2. Identify the cause of stress.
3. Do something about the cause of stress.
4. Take action to reduce the harmful effects of stress.

Use communication skills.

1. Choose the best way to communicate.
2. Send a clear message. Be polite.
3. Listen to the other person.
4. Make sure you understand each other.

Access valid health information, products, and services.

1. Identify when you need health information, products, and services.
2. Identify where you can find health information, products, and services.
3. Locate health information, products, and services.
4. Evaluate what you found.

Use resistance skills.

1. Say "no" in a firm voice.
2. Give reasons for saying "no."
3. Be certain your behavior matches your words.
4. Ask an adult for help if you need help.

Resolve conflicts.

1. Stay calm.
2. Talk about the conflict.
3. Discuss possible ways to settle the conflict.
4. Agree on a way to settle the conflict. You may need to ask a trusted adult for help.

Set health goals.

1. Write the health goal you want to set.
2. Explain how the goal will affect your health.
3. Describe a plan you will follow. Keep track of your progress.
4. Evaluate how your plan worked.

Be a health advocate.

1. Select a health-related concern to communicate.
2. Gather reliable information.
3. Identify your purpose and target audience.
4. Develop a convincing and appropriate message.

Make responsible decisions.

1. Identify your choices. Check them out with your parent or another trusted adult.
2. Evaluate each choice. Use the Guidelines for Making Responsible Decisions.™ Answer only the questions that apply to this situation.
3. Tell what the responsible decision is. Check this out with your parent or another trusted adult.
4. Evaluate your decision.

Guidelines for Making Responsible Decisions™

- ☑ Is it healthful?
- ☑ Is it safe?
- ☑ Is it legal?
- ☑ Do I show respect for myself and others?
- ☑ Do I follow the guidelines of responsible adults such as my parents or guardian?
- ☑ Do I demonstrate good character?

You will learn...

- ways to express thoughts and feelings honestly and directly.

- how to use I-messages and active listening.

- how to avoid sending mixed messages.

- ways to resolve conflicts with others.

Communication

Relationships are the interactions you have with other people. Imagine a life without relationships! You would not have anyone with whom to share your accomplishments. You would not have anyone to cheer you up when you are down. You would not have anyone with whom you could talk on the phone or hang out.

This book is about building healthful relationships. Healthful relationships are relationships that promote mutual respect and responsible behavior. This chapter describes communication skills that you can use to develop healthful relationships.

VOCABULARY

- relationships, 3
- healthful relationships, 3
- communication, 4
- aggressive communication style, 5
- passive communication style, 5
- assertive communication style, 5
- I-message, 6
- empathy, 7
- active listening, 8
- nonverbal communication, 8
- mixed message, 8
- conflict, 9
- conflict resolution skills, 9
- mediation, 10
- body language, 10

Your Communication Style

Communication is the sharing of feelings, thoughts, and information with others. There are different styles and types of communication. Complete the *Communication Style Checkout* below to gain insight about your particular style of communicating. Number a sheet of paper from 1 to 5. Read each of the following situations. Select the answer that best describes how you would respond. On your paper, write the letter of the answer beside the corresponding number.

Communication Style Checkout

1. **Your friend stops speaking to you and you have no idea why. You feel upset about the way she is treating you.**
   a. You blame her for acting dumb for no reason and tell her you don't want to be around anyone like her.
   b. You avoid her at school but wonder what happened.
   c. You tell her that you are hurt by her actions and ask for an explanation. You say, "I want to fix this but I can't until I know what it's about."

2. **At the last minute, your mother cancels a camping trip you were looking forward to.**
   a. You yell, "You never care about what I want. I can never count on you!" and stomp off to your room.
   b. You say, "I don't care. I didn't really want to go much, anyway."
   c. You tell your mother you are very disappointed and ask if she can reschedule the camping trip.

3. **Your cousin tells a classmate about something you did that really embarrassed you. Your cousin had promised not to tell anyone.**
   a. You find your cousin, get angry at her, and tell her she is a blabbermouth and that you will never trust her again.
   b. You try to laugh off the story to your classmate but say nothing to your cousin.
   c. You tell your cousin that you are upset that she broke her promise and feel angry that she caused you such embarrassment.

4. **You and a friend have plans to go to a concert together. When you get to his house, he says he changed his mind and wants to go to the mall instead. You really want to go to the concert.**
   a. You tell your friend he never keeps his word and you will have a better time at the concert without him.
   b. You say, "Okay, I guess I could go to the mall, too."
   c. You tell your friend that you really want to go to the concert. You suggest that he go to the concert with you tonight as planned, and that he choose what to do the next time.

5. **Your friend is upset because his pet snake has died. You are not a big fan of snakes and are relieved that the snake is gone.**
   a. You explain that the snake gave you the creeps, and anyway it wasn't a real pet like a cat or dog.
   b. You say, "Yeah, I'll really miss him, too," and try to change the topic.
   c. You tell your friend that you know the snake meant a lot to him and you are sorry he is upset.

Aggressive Communication Style

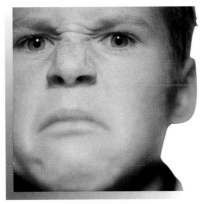

If you answered "a" to most of the situations, you may be in the habit of using an aggressive communication style. People who have an **aggressive communication style** express anger using you-messages to blame and to accuse others. They might say "You are to blame." or "If you were paying attention, you would understand." They usually are unwilling to compromise.

Passive Communication Style

If you answered "b" to most of the situations, you may have developed a passive communication style. People who have a **passive communication style** are uncomfortable letting their needs, wants, or opinions be known. They often withdraw and hold back the truth rather than say what is on their mind.

Assertive Communication Style

If you answered "c" to most of the situations, you may have an assertive communication style. People who have an **assertive communication style** express their thoughts and feelings in an honest and direct manner. They do so in a way that shows respect for the rights of others. Assertive communicators tend to use I-messages to say what they feel, need, and want. Their communication style is the one that best promotes healthful relationships.

Using I-Messages

Perhaps you would like to use the honest and direct assertive communication style more often but don't know where to begin. The first step is to make a habit of using I-messages.

An **I-message** is a statement that describes:

1. A specific behavior or event.
2. The effect that the behavior or event has on you.
3. The feelings that you have as a result.

When you use I-messages, you say "This is what *I* experienced," "This is how *I* feel," and sometimes "This is what *I* need or want to happen." The focus is on you. This honest and direct communication style is the opposite of an aggressive communication style. People who have an aggressive communication style focus on the other person. They might say, "This is what *you* did," "This is what *you* are," or "This is what *your* problem is." People who have a passive communication style are fearful and focus on hiding their thoughts and feelings. Inside they feel stressed and angry. Their anger builds and at some point they may not be able to control it. Have you ever seen a person who seemed passive explode? I-messages are an effective tool in building healthful relationships. The following are situations in which you might use I-messages.

When you are hurt or angry

Have you ever had plans to go to a movie with a friend and your friend canceled at the last minute? Your friend called to say that he or she did not feel well. The next day a classmate says that she was at a party last night and your friend was there. Use the following I-message:

1. **I heard you went to a party after canceling our plans.**

   (describes a specific behavior or event)

2. **After you called to tell me you were sick, I stayed home. It was too late to ask someone else to go.**

   (describes the effect the behavior or event had on you)

3. **I am hurt and upset that my evening was ruined, and disappointed that you didn't tell me the truth.**

   (describes the feelings that you have as a result)

This I-message opens the door for communication. Your friend knows what is bothering you and how you feel. Now your friend can respond to the situation and to your feelings.

6

When you are insecure or afraid

Have you ever been invited to a party where you will not know anyone? You might be uneasy about going. If you want support from your parents or guardian, you need to share your concerns. Use the following I-message in a conversation with them:

1. **I got an invitation to a party. I won't know anyone there.**

   (describes a specific behavior or event)

2. **I'm worried that I won't know what to say to anyone.**

   (describes the effect the behavior or event had on you)

3. **I want to go, but I'm afraid I won't fit in.**

   (describes the feelings that you have as a result)

By using this I-message to communicate your feelings, you help your parents or guardian realize your need for support. Once they know what is bothering you and how you feel, they can have empathy for you. **Empathy** is the ability to share in what another person is feeling. They might show empathy by telling you how they have dealt with a similar situation. They may help build your self-confidence about going to the party. They can help you make a decision about the party that will make you comfortable.

When you really care for someone

Suppose your aunt is very ill. Your parents have told you she will not live much longer. You know you are going to miss her very much. You want her to know how much you care. Use the following I-message:

1. **Some of the best times I've ever had have been with you. Now my parents say that you are very sick.**

   (describes a specific behavior or event)

2. **I love you so much and I will miss you.**

   (describes the effect the behavior or event had on you)

3. **I'm so sad.**

   (describes the feelings that you have as a result)

It is hard to express feelings about death. However, an I-message can help you share your feelings. Your aunt will feel comforted to know how much you care. She can express her love in return, which can comfort you. You will be glad you made the effort to communicate during this difficult time. Even if you aren't sure of what to say, you will never regret that you spoke in an honest and direct manner when you had the chance.

Being a Good Listener

There is a balance of communication in healthful relationships. Sometimes you are the talker. Other times you are the listener. How you listen makes a difference. **Active listening** is a type of listening in which a person lets others know that he or she heard and understood what was said.

Four Ways to Use Active Listening

1. **Ask for more information.**
2. **Repeat what the other person said using your own words.**
3. **Summarize the main ideas expressed.**
4. **Acknowledge the feelings that the person expressed and thank the person for sharing his or her feelings.**

Avoiding Mixed Messages

Have you ever heard the saying "Actions speak louder than words"? **Nonverbal communication** is the use of actions rather than words to express thoughts and feelings. For example, you are on the winning soccer team and you give your teammate a high five. This action expresses your joy in winning. You don't need words.

If your sister was crying, you might reach out and put your arm around her. Your action expresses comfort and tells her you care. There are many forms of nonverbal communication. If you dislike what someone is doing, you might frown. When things are going right, you might smile or give a thumbs-up sign. If you don't know an answer or if you really don't care about something you just heard, you might shrug your shoulders.

Avoid sending mixed messages when you communicate. A **mixed message** is a message that conveys two different meanings. There are two kinds of mixed messages to avoid.

1. Your words and nonverbal actions convey two different meanings.
2. Your words and tone of voice convey two different meanings.

The Mixed Message Quiz

Have you ever . . .

1. . . . congratulated your friends when they did well, but did so with a jealous tone in your voice?

2. . . . told your parent that you didn't mind doing a chore, but rolled your eyes as you spoke?

3. . . . agreed with a teacher that what he was saying was serious and important, but kept grinning at your friends?

If you answered "yes" to any of the above questions, you have sent a mixed message.

Resolving Conflicts

A **conflict** is a disagreement between two or more people or between two or more choices. Many conflicts between people are the result of poor communication. Others occur when people do not treat one another with respect. Do your best to avoid conflicts. Act in a thoughtful, considerate way and try to communicate in an honest and direct manner. If conflicts do occur, you can use conflict resolution skills to keep them from getting worse. **Conflict resolution skills** are steps to take to resolve a disagreement in a responsible and nonviolent way.

Four Steps to Resolve a Conflict

1. Stay calm.
- Try to control angry feelings.
- Do not blame or shame, interrupt, or use put-downs or threats.

2. Talk about the conflict.
- Define the conflict.
- Use I-messages and active listening.
- Listen to what the other person has to say about what happened and how he or she feels about it.
- Tell what you think happened and how you feel about it.

3. Discuss possible ways to settle the conflict. Use the Guidelines for Making Responsible Decisions™ to evaluate each possible way. Ask these questions:
- Is it healthful?
- Is it safe?
- Is it legal?
- Does it allow me to show respect for myself and others?
- Does it allow me to follow the guidelines of responsible adults, such as my parents or guardian?
- Does it allow me to demonstrate good character?

4. Agree on a way to settle the conflict. You may need to ask a trusted adult for help.
- Brainstorm to arrive at a fair solution that meets with everyone's approval.
- Commit yourself to doing what you agree to do.

1. **I am very shy. I am afraid to meet new people and have trouble communicating with them when I do meet them. How can I deal with my shyness?**

   You have already begun to deal with your shyness by admitting your fears. Now it is time for you to face those fears. Since you are afraid to meet new people and have trouble talking with new acquaintances, you might consider joining a school club or trying out for a play or sport. The people will be new to you but you will all have something in common to talk about.

2. **I finally got up the nerve to ask a girl in my math class to go to next Saturday's basketball game with me. She turned me down and now I feel like such a loser. How can I face anyone again?**

   Everyone has to face rejection now and then. The first thing you need to do is not overreact. This is one person saying "no" to one invitation. Try not to dwell on this incident. Make a point of spending time with the friends you are closest to for a while. Also, share your disappointment with a parent, guardian, or another trusted adult.

3. **My friend asked me what I thought of her new short haircut. I told her it was ugly and made her look like a little boy. Now she won't speak to me. I thought being direct and honest and using an assertive communication style was supposed to help build healthful relationships. What went wrong?**

   Expressing your thoughts and feelings in an honest and direct manner is only part of an assertive communication style. The other part is respecting the rights of others. Being honest does not mean having to share every thought that you have. The next time a situation like this comes up, you might say something like, "Wow, a totally new style. Are you liking it this short?"

4. **I know I have an aggressive communication style, but I get angry so easily. How can I change?**

   Anger management skills can help you express anger in an assertive, not aggressive, way. Try these steps to start. 1. Do what it takes to keep calm. Try taking deep breaths or counting to ten before you speak. 2. Use I-messages to express your feelings. 3. Talk through your feelings with a parent, guardian, or another trusted adult.

5. **What is mediation?**

   Mediation is a process in which an uninvolved third party helps people involved in a conflict reach a responsible solution. The uninvolved person is called a mediator. The mediator listens to both points of view without taking sides. The mediator is not a judge. He or she simply helps both sides listen to each other and come up with a responsible solution to the conflict.

6. **What is body language?**

   Body language is a form of nonverbal communication that includes facial expressions, hand and foot movements, touching, posture, and the presence or absence of eye contact. Clenching your teeth, tapping your toe, and raising your eyebrows are all examples of body language. You may or may not be aware of the message you are sending with your body.

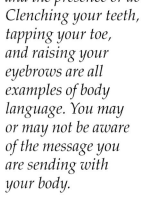

Use Vocabulary

Complete each sentence by choosing the term from the list below that best fits in the blank. Write your answers on a separate sheet of paper.

active listening	empathy	relationships
conflict	nonverbal communication	

1. The ability to share in what another person is feeling is known as _____?_____.

2. Nodding your head to show you understand while another person speaks is an example of _____?_____.

3. The use of actions rather than words to express thoughts and feelings is called _____?_____.

4. Your interactions with other people are called your _____?_____.

5. A disagreement between two or more people or two or more choices is called a(n) _____?_____.

Review Concepts

Write your answers to the following questions on a separate sheet of paper.

6. Blaming and accusing the other person is an example of which communication style?

7. What are the drawbacks of having a passive communication style?

8. How does having an assertive communication style promote healthful relationships?

9. What does an I-message describe?

10. What is the difference between using I-messages and using you-messages?

11. What are four ways to use active listening?

12. What are some examples of nonverbal communication?

13. What are two kinds of mixed messages to avoid?

14. What are two reasons conflict occurs?

15. What are the four steps to follow to resolve conflict?

Critical Thinking/Problem Solving

Write your responses to the following questions and statements on a separate sheet of paper.

16. Describe a situation in which you used a passive or an aggressive communication style. How might the situation have been different if you had used an assertive communication style?

17. Write an I-message in which you share your feelings about a friend who did not fulfill a promise to help you plan a party.

18. Discuss the problems you might face if you sent a mixed message. How would a situation have been improved if you sent a consistent message?

Practice Life Skills

19. **Set Health Goals** Describe a plan to improve your listening skills.

2

You will learn...

- responsible values that make up good character and reasons why you need to have good character.

- how to use the *Guidelines for Making Responsible Decisions™*.

- resistance skills to say "no" if you are pressured to choose a wrong action.

- what steps to take to correct wrong actions.

- how to choose friends who have good character.

- how to work to achieve balanced relationships.

- how to recognize and do something about abusive relationships.

Good Character in Relationships

Suppose a store clerk gives you back too much change. You really could use the money. A friend tells you: "It's a big store. They won't miss it." What would you do? The action you choose in a situation like this is a measure of your character.

This chapter teaches you how to develop good character. **Good character** is the use of self-control to act on responsible values. **Self-control** is the effort you make to resist temptation. A **responsible value** is a belief that guides you to act in responsible ways.

The choice that shows good character in the above situation is to point out the clerk's mistake and give the extra change back.

VOCABULARY

- **good character,** 13
- **self-control,** 13
- **responsible value,** 13
- **honesty,** 14
- **respect,** 14
- **responsibility,** 14
- **fairness,** 14
- **caring,** 14
- **citizenship,** 15
- **self-discipline,** 15
- **abstinence from sex,** 15
- **determination,** 15
- **courage,** 15
- **integrity,** 15
- **self-respect,** 16
- **reputation,** 16
- **conscience,** 16
- **Guidelines for Making Responsible Decisions™,** 17
- **peer pressure,** 18
- **resistance skills,** 18
- **sorry,** 19
- **punishment,** 19
- **restitution,** 19
- **pay back,** 19
- **pay forward,** 19
- **balanced relationship,** 21
- **one-sided relationship,** 21
- **control freak,** 21
- **doormat,** 21
- **abuse,** 22
- **neglect, 22**
- **physical abuse,** 22
- **emotional abuse,** 22
- **sexual abuse,** 22
- **mentor,** 23

Signs of Good Character

The way you will respond to a difficult, bothersome, or tempting situation is a sign of your character. Read each of the following situations.

Select the answer that you think demonstrates good character. Check the column on the right to see if your choice demonstrates good character.

HONESTY

1. The answers for tomorrow's test are on your teacher's desk. The teacher has left the room for a few minutes.
   a. You step back away from the desk without reading the answers.
   b. You read what you can from where you are.

If you chose "a," your actions show that you are honest. **Honesty** is always telling the truth to the best of your knowledge, playing by the rules, and not cheating. Being honest is a sign of good character.

RESPECT

2. You go to an amusement park with classmates. One classmate is afraid of heights and won't ride the roller coaster.
   a. You make jokes about the classmate's fear.
   b. You ask the classmate to wait while you ride the roller coaster and offer to ride whatever he wants next.

If you chose "b," you show respect. **Respect** is treating others with dignity, being considerate of others' feelings, and being tolerant of people's differences and beliefs. Showing respect is a sign of good character.

RESPONSIBILITY

3. You accidentally scratch your friend's favorite CD.
   a. You tell your friend what happened and apologize.
   b. You say that you did not scratch the CD.

If you chose "a," you are responsible. **Responsibility** is being accountable for your actions. Responsible people apologize and try to make it up to the person they have harmed. Responsibility is a sign of good character.

FAIRNESS

4. A new student at school was assigned to help in your project team. You do not know her, but she says she has a new idea about the project.
   a. You brush her off and turn away.
   b. You practice active listening while she speaks.

If you chose "b," your actions show that you are fair. **Fairness** is showing equal courtesy and respect to everyone. Being fair is a sign of good character.

CARING

5. The bell is about to ring and everyone is hurrying to class. Someone you do not know trips. His papers and books scatter.
   a. You step over the mess and hurry on.
   b. You stop and help pick up his stuff and ask if he is hurt.

If you chose "b," you show that you care. **Caring** is feeling empathy for those who are in pain or distress. Caring people try to help those in trouble if they can and try hard not to harm anyone. Caring is a sign of good character.

CITIZENSHIP

6. You are hurrying to school. At the corner, you see that someone has knocked down the stop sign that is usually there. It needs to be standing upright to be seen.

   a. You realize this may be dangerous but do nothing about it and hurry on to school.

   b. You call the police to report the damaged sign.

If you chose "b," your actions show good citizenship. **Citizenship** is obeying the laws and doing your part to make your community a better place to live. Citizenship is a sign of good character.

SELF-DISCIPLINE

7. You have a test in two days. Your friends want you to go to the movies with them tonight.

   a. You go along and cram for the test tomorrow.

   b. You stay home to study for the test.

If you chose "b," your actions show that you have self-discipline. **Self-discipline** is the effort you make to follow through with a task—such as a promise you made or a goal you set. Being self-disciplined is a sign of good character.

ABSTINENCE FROM SEX

8. Someone is pressuring you to be sexually active.

   a. You give in to the pressure.

   b. You say "no" and stick to your decision.

If you chose "b," you practice abstinence from sex. **Abstinence from sex** is choosing not to be sexually active. Choosing abstinence from sex helps you keep self-respect and the respect of others. Practicing abstinence from sex is a sign of good character.

DETERMINATION

9. Your skills have improved this year and you really enjoy the sport but you didn't make the team.

   a. You plan to keep improving and try out next year.

   b. You decide to give up.

If you chose "a," your behavior shows determination. **Determination** is working hard to get what you want. Having determination is a sign of good character.

COURAGE

10. You do not understand the math problem the teacher just explained.

    a. You keep quiet so no one thinks you are "dumb."

    b. You ask the teacher to explain it again.

If you chose "b," you show courage. **Courage** is showing strength when you might otherwise be afraid. Showing courage is a sign of good character.

INTEGRITY

11. You go to a party with some friends. When you get there you see several teens drinking beer.

    a. You carry a can of beer around and pretend to drink to fit in with the crowd.

    b. You leave the party.

If you chose "b," you have integrity. **Integrity** is acting on responsible values regardless of the consequences. Having integrity is a sign of good character.

15

Reasons to Have Good Character

There are many reasons to develop good character. Which of the reasons below are most important to you?

- **To have self-respect** Self-respect is a high regard for oneself as a result of behaving in responsible ways. You develop self-respect when you make responsible decisions and try to do the right thing.

- **To get along with my parents or guardians** Your parents or guardians expect you to follow their guidelines. Acting against their guidelines results in unpleasantness for both of you. Show your respect for your parents or guardians by following their guidelines.

- **To keep the respect of others** Showing respect is important, but you also want other people to respect you. You can earn the respect of your peers and the adults in your life by acting in responsible ways. After you earn respect, you must work to keep it.

- **To protect my future** Your character affects the actions you take now. Those actions can also affect your future. Good character can help you move ahead in life and help you accomplish things such as going to college, getting a job, and having a family.

- **To stay out of trouble** Your reputation is the quality of your character as judged by others. People with good reputations are trusted and respected. Showing signs of good character will help you build a good reputation. On the other hand, wrong actions can have serious consequences. They harm your reputation.

- **To keep a clear conscience** Your conscience is your inner sense of right and wrong. When you hesitate because something inside is telling you that what you are considering is wrong, that is your conscience talking. Take steps to correct the wrong action.

The Guidelines for Making Responsible Decisions™

The next time you are making a decision, follow four steps to help ensure that you make a responsible decision. Begin by stating to yourself what the situation is that requires a decision. State the situation as clearly as you can. Then make a responsible decision by following these four steps.

1. **Identify the choices. Check them out with your parent or another trusted adult.**

2. **Evaluate each choice. Use the Guidelines for Making Responsible Decisions™.** The Guidelines for Making Responsible Decisions™ are six questions that you can ask to ensure that the decision you make is responsible. Not all of the questions listed in the *Guidelines* will apply to every possible choice. Use the *Guidelines* that apply to your situation. Whenever possible, share this step with parents or guardians.

3. **Tell what the responsible decision is. Check this out with your parent or another trusted adult.** Base your decision on the choice to which you answered "yes" for each question you asked.

4. **Evaluate your decision.** What happened as a result—or what do you think is most likely to happen?

Guidelines for Making Responsible Decisions™

- **Is it healthful?**
- **Is it safe?**
- **Is it legal?**
- **Do I show respect for myself and others?**
- **Do I follow the guidelines of responsible adults, such as my parents or guardian?**
- **Do I demonstrate good character?**

Your decision will not be responsible if you answer "no" to any of the six questions that apply.

Saying "No"

Peer pressure is the influence that people of similar age or status place on others to encourage them to make certain decisions or behave in certain ways. During the teen years, peer pressure can be a major influence on a person's behavior. That influence can be either positive or negative. Friends who have good character can be a positive influence. They will encourage you to make responsible decisions and practice healthful behaviors. They will not pressure you to do anything against your values. On the other hand, friends who don't have good character can be a negative influence. They are likely to pressure you to do things that you know are wrong.

Your peers can pressure you, but your behavior is your responsibility. Be proud of who you are and what you stand for. When being pressured to do something wrong, stand firm, look the person in the eye, and say "no." Use resistance skills to help you stick to your values. **Resistance skills** are skills that are used when a person wants to say "no" to an action or to leave a situation. They are also called *refusal skills.* The following is what you should do.

1. **Say "no" in a firm voice.** Show confidence and look directly at the person who is pressuring you. Let the person know your limits. Do not apologize for your decisions. Do not be afraid to be loud and direct.

2. **Give reasons for saying "no."** Use the six Guidelines for Making Responsible Decisions™ as your reasons for saying "no." These reasons should state the effects of the risk behavior to your health, safety, the law, self-respect and respect for others, your family guidelines, and good character.

3. **Be certain your behavior matches your words.** Do not let your decision be influenced by those who choose risk behaviors. Avoid situations in which there will be pressure for you to do something wrong. Avoid being with people who do not have good character. Do not send mixed messages.

4. **Ask an adult for help if you need help.** Talk to a parent, guardian, or another responsible adult if you need help resisting risk behaviors.

Correcting Wrong Actions

When you make a wrong decision, other people may let you know. They may show disappointment or anger or just offer guidance. Often you already know when you have taken wrong actions because your conscience nags you. To regain trust and clear your conscience, you must correct the wrong action. Follow these steps to make things right.

1 **Take responsibility for what you have done.** Do not try to cover up wrong actions. Do not bother making excuses. Never blame someone else. These actions just make matters worse. Be honest. People respect honesty.

2 **Apologize and pledge to not do the wrong action again.** Be sincere and show that you are sorry. Being **sorry** is an expression of apology or regret. Being sorry and meaning it can help you rebuild trust.

3 **Discuss the wrong action with a parent, guardian, or another responsible adult.** Sharing the facts with a parent or another trusted adult may seem like asking for trouble, but it is really asking for help. Adults may help you understand the reasons for your wrong actions. They can help you decide on ways to correct what you have done. Adults can give you the support and guidance you need to make things right.

4 **Accept appropriate punishment.** Wrong actions have negative consequences. Depending on the action, the consequences may include punishment. **Punishment** is a penalty for wrongdoing. Accepting appropriate punishment can help "clean the slate" and allow you to get back on track and move on.

5 **Make restitution.** **Restitution** is making good for any loss, damage, or injury. An apology cannot replace lost or damaged property. Nor does it pay medical bills. Sometimes you have to pay money or to work to pay for the loss your wrong action caused. There are two types of restitution: To **pay back** is to make restitution to a person or persons who suffered a loss due to your actions. To **pay forward** is to make restitution to society. Restitution to society may include legal proceedings. It may include a fine, required counseling, supervision, or confinement.

Choosing Friends Who Have Good Character

Always choose friends who have good character. When you are around people who demonstrate good character traits, they will influence you to have good character. You keep a good reputation when you stick with friends who have good character. Here are tips to help you choose friends who have good character.

Show good character yourself. Good character is like a magnet. Act on the responsible values that make up good character and you will attract friends of good character.

Listen to the advice responsible adults give you about friends. Your parents, guardian, and other responsible adults know what makes up good character. They have had plenty of experience in spotting good and bad character in others.

Use the *Good Character Checklist* below to help you choose friends. Suppose you really like someone who has major character flaws. The questions on the Checklist will help you stay objective. When someone has major character flaws, you know what to do—stay away.

Your answers should be "yes" for each question on the *Good Character Checklist*.

Good Character Checklist for Choosing Friends

YES NO

☑ ☐ Do my parents or guardian approve of this person?

☑ ☐ Does this person choose other friends who show good character?

☑ ☐ Does this person act on responsible values?

☑ ☐ Does this person communicate in an open and honest way?

☑ ☐ Does this person treat me and others with respect?

☑ ☐ Is this person nonviolent?

☑ ☐ Does this person make responsible decisions?

☑ ☐ Does this person successfully practice resistance skills when pressured to choose harmful actions?

☑ ☐ Does this person take steps to correct wrong actions?

☑ ☐ Does this person practice abstinence from sex?

☑ ☐ Does this person refuse to use harmful and illegal drugs?

☑ ☐ Does this person obey laws?

Balance in Your Relationships

A healthful friendship is a **balanced relationship**, one based on give-and-take. There is a balance of power. Both friends have and show respect for each other. They care about each other and they support each other. One person does not do all the giving while the other does the taking.

Suppose you have a best friend. Sometimes your friend needs you to listen. You practice active listening skills when your friend talks. At other times, your friend puts your needs first. For example, you might ask your friend to change plans to help you with a project. In a balanced relationship, you and the other person are willing to be flexible and to sometimes put the other person's needs ahead of your own. You share the power in the relationship.

The opposite of a balanced relationship is a **one-sided relationship**, which is a relationship in which one person has most of the power. This person is almost always taking. The other person is almost always giving. He or she must always accommodate the demands of the taker. You may hear people in one-sided relationships described, depending on their role, as a control freak or a doormat.

A **control freak** is a person who wants all the power in a relationship. He or she wants to always be in control of what the other person says or does or even thinks. Control freaks are often jealous and quick to be offended and angry. Control freaks are not sincerely concerned about the feelings or needs of other people. Their actions are always self-serving.

A **doormat** is a person who gives all of the power in a relationship to the other person. Another name for doormats is people pleasers. Doormats want approval more than anything else. They don't have enough self-respect to stand up for themselves.

Unbalanced relationships are often between a control freak and a doormat. They each fill one another's needs. The control freak is focused on meeting his or her own needs, so he or she bullies the doormat. The doormat takes it all without objecting because he or she is focused on being accepted. Unbalanced relationships are not healthful for anyone. The relationship needs to be changed. To have good character, you must have balanced relationships.

Abuse in Relationships

Abuse is the harmful treatment of another person. Abuse can be between peers, between an older child and a younger child, and between an adult and a child or a teen. Abuse can happen in families.

Abuse is *always* wrong. No one ever deserves to be abused. Abuse can be stopped, but first it must be recognized. Listed below are behaviors that may signal one of the four kinds of abuse.

How to Spot Abuse

Neglect is failure to provide for a person's basic physical and emotional needs.
Red flags for neglect include:

- Failing to supervise children
- Failing to provide family guidelines
- Failing to appropriately discipline children for wrong actions
- Failing to provide nutritious food
- Failing to provide secure and healthful shelter
- Failing to provide necessary medical care
- Failing to send children to school
- Ignoring the needs and wants of children

Physical Abuse is harmful treatment of a person that results in physical injury or pain.
Red flags for physical abuse include:

- Hitting, slapping, punching, or kicking
- Stabbing
- Pinching
- Scratching with fingernails
- Pulling hair
- Shoving or pushing
- Grabbing
- Holding against will
- Burning or cutting

Emotional Abuse is making a person feel worthless or unimportant by putting him or her down.
Red flags for emotional abuse include:

- Constantly criticizing
- Withholding praise for good work
- Never being satisfied no matter how hard the person tries
- Stalking
- Bullying or threatening
- Ignoring a person
- Calling the person obscene or degrading names in person, by phone, or by e-mail

Sexual Abuse is sexual activity that is forced on a person or occurs before the legal age of consent. Legal age varies from state to state.
Red flags for sexual abuse include:

- Making unwanted sexual advances
- Touching in ways the other person does not want to be touched
- Making unwanted sexual comments
- Teasing in a sexual way
- Making sexual threats
- Making sexually suggestive phone calls or e-mails
- Rape
- Having sex with a person under the legal age of consent

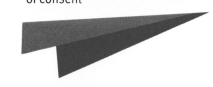

How to Stop Abuse

1. **Tell the person to stop the abusive behavior.** Confronting a person is usually effective for stopping emotional abuse. It can also work for other kinds of abuse, but you have to evaluate each situation. Be cautious. Skip this step if you think that telling the person who is causing the abuse to stop might make him or her abuse you more.

2. **Tell a responsible adult.** Responsible adults can help you find ways to stop all four kinds of abuse.

3. **Find a mentor.** A mentor is a responsible person who guides another person. People who might make a good mentor include parents, guardians, teachers, coaches, youth leaders, counselors, and religious leaders. A mentor should be a role model who can help you develop good character traits. Choose a mentor who shows good character. Choose a mentor who can help you develop self-respect and help you resolve conflicts without violence.

4. **Join a support group.** A support group can be a safe place to share feelings. Here, you can discuss your feelings and behavior with other teens who have been abused.

5. **Do not use risk behaviors to cope or get attention.** Some people turn to risk behaviors when they feel they cannot stop abuse or the memory of past abuse. They may be hoping that someone will notice the risk behavior and help them. They may hope the risk behavior will make them forget the abuse they experienced or their fear of future abuse. Smoking, drinking alcohol, taking drugs, harming oneself, or becoming sexually active will make a situation worse. Failing your classes, dropping out of school, becoming a teen parent, or breaking the law will make a present situation worse and can ruin one's future. Risk behaviors are not a solution. Instead, look again at steps 1 to 4.

6. **Evaluate your own behavior and stop the cycle of abuse.** The cycle of abuse occurs when a person who has been abused abuses other people. Sometimes young people who are regularly abused begin to think that abuse is a normal part of life. A teen who is beaten at home might make a habit of dealing with people at school by hitting or punching. Abuse is never acceptable behavior. It is always wrong. Having been abused is never an excuse for committing abuse. Always remember to treat others the way you want to be treated.

1. **I want to have good character. I made up a list of rules for myself so I could develop self-discipline. I really try hard, but I always seem to slip up somewhere. What can I do to stop failing?**

   To develop good character, you need to set realistic standards. A realistic standard is a requirement a person sets for himself or herself that can be reasonably achieved. The key word is realistic. *If you have set standards for yourself that cannot be reasonably achieved, you have set yourself up to fail. Rethink your goals. If you continue to have difficulty, talk to your parents, guardian, or another responsible adult. They can help you set realistic standards.*

2. **How do I know if my friendship with a certain person is a healthful friendship?**

   There are five qualities that characterize a healthful friendship. The first is trust: Good friends in a healthful relationship trust each other. They are comfortable confiding in each other because they know their trust will not be betrayed. The second quality is reliability: Good friends know they can depend on each other, no matter what happens. The third quality is empathy: Good friends are able to identify with, and share, each other's feelings and concerns. The fourth quality is caring: Good friends truly care about each other. The fifth quality is respect. Good friends value each other's opinions and decisions.

3. **My mother says she doesn't have the same friends now that she did when she was in high school. She says that I'll "outgrow" some of my friends, too. I feel so close to my friends. I can't think of them ever NOT being around. Will I lose some of my friends, too, someday?**

   While some friendships become stronger over time, others simply end or fade away for many different reasons. Friends may move away, and

you may lose touch. You may go to a new school and find a new set of friends. You may meet people who more clearly share your interests as you become an adult. A friend may reveal a secret that you shared or, in some other way, disappoint you, and your friendship will not be the same after that. A friend might pressure you to choose risk behaviors or make decisions that are not responsible. A friend may become abusive or start to use drugs. Changing friends is a normal part of life. The important thing to remember is that, as you get older, you will make new friends to take the place of those with whom you do not stay close.*

4. **What things can happen to a person who has been or is being abused?**

   Being abused can affect every aspect of the person's life. Being abused might make a person feel angry, fearful, confused, and depressed. Being abused might cause a person to have trouble concentrating or to feel isolated and distrustful of others. Some people who are abused might misuse or abuse alcohol or other drugs or engage in other self-destructive behaviors. Those who are abused often have negative self-esteem. They might feel embarrassed, ashamed, and worthless. They might believe that there is something wrong with them, or that they have done something wrong, for the abuse to happen. Because of these mistaken ideas, people who are abused might not report the abuse or take action to stop the abuse.

5. **How can a person find out where to get help locally if he or she is being abused?**

   A person could look in the community pages of the telephone book under Health and Human Services to find places he or she can call for information.

Use Vocabulary

Complete each sentence by choosing the term from the list below that best fits in the blank. Write your answers on a separate sheet of paper.

citizenship	mentor	self-control
integrity	restitution	

1. A responsible person who guides another person is called a(n) _____?_____.

2. When you act on responsible values regardless of the consequences, you are showing _____?_____.

3. When you make good for any loss, damage, or injury you caused, you are making _____?_____.

4. The effort you make to resist temptation is known as _____?_____.

5. Obeying the laws and doing your part to make your community a better place to live is called _____?_____.

Review Concepts

Write your answers to the following questions on a separate sheet of paper.

6. What are six of the eleven responsible values that show you have good character?

7. What are six reasons to have good character?

8. What are the six questions in the Guidelines for Making Responsible Decisions™?

9. What are four resistance skills that will help you stick to a decision to say "no"?

10. What are five steps you can take to correct wrong actions?

11. What are tips to help you choose friends who have good character?

12. How can you spot a control freak?

13. How can you spot a doormat?

14. What are four kinds of abuse that can damage relationships?

15. What six things can you do to stop abuse?

Critical Thinking/Problem Solving

Write your responses to the following questions and statements on a separate sheet of paper.

16. You want to help out at a day camp. You are asked to get a letter of recommendation from an adult. The letter is to discuss your character. Write a sample letter. Discuss at least three signs of good character that you regularly demonstrate.

17. You had a friend who lied to you and when you confronted him or her, the friend promised not to lie to you again. Later you caught the friend in another lie. What would you do?

Practice Life Skills

18. **Analyze What Influences Your Health** You have learned responsible values that make up good character. Identify responsible adults who demonstrate these values. They may be public figures or people from your town. How have they influenced you to show good character?

3

You will learn...

- how to spend quality time with family members.

- why following your family's guidelines is important.

- how to make healthful adjustments to family changes.

- how to recognize and improve difficult family relationships.

Make Family Life a Priority

Although the teen years are an exciting time, being a teen has its challenges. Healthful family relationships can provide the support and comfort you need to meet your daily challenges. **Healthful family relationships** are relationships in which family members relate well, show respect for one another, and behave in responsible ways. Having healthful relationships with your family can make you feel valued and loved. Your family can help you increase your confidence and the self-respect you need to deal with the ups and downs of teen life. Family members can also supply valuable guidance. They can show you how to act in responsible ways, and they can guide you to avoid situations and individuals likely to put you at risk.

This chapter teaches you about family relationships and the things that can affect them. You will also learn ways to develop and maintain healthful relationships with your family members.

VOCABULARY

- healthful family relationships, 27
- unnecessary risk, 28
- calculated risk, 28
- gender role, 28
- family guidelines, 29
- marital separation, 30
- divorce, 30
- remarriage, 30
- blended family, 30
- premature death, 31
- stress, 32
- dysfunctional family, 33
- drug dependence, 33
- addiction, 33
- abuse, 33
- violence, 33
- domestic violence, 33
- abandonment, 33
- recovery program, 33

Spending Time with Your Family

Part of being a teen is being busy. With a busy schedule, you must be careful not to neglect your family. You need to make family life a priority. There are good reasons to spend time with your family.

To fulfill your need to belong

Wanting to belong is a basic human need. Your family is a good place to fulfill that need. Family members can supply love, support, and encouragement. They can share in your joys and help you through difficult situations. What might it be like for teens who are not close to their families? They might feel empty and lonely. They may try to rely on peers to fulfill their need to belong. Friends are important, but it is risky to put peers ahead of family. Peers simply do not have the experience and wisdom of adults. Also, unlike your parents or guardian, your peers are not responsible for you. They do not have to be concerned about your future. They may not always have your long-term best interests at heart.

To practice taking calculated risks in a safe setting

An **unnecessary risk** is a chance not worth taking after you consider the possible outcomes. It is an action that might jeopardize your own and others' health and safety. Getting into a car driven by someone who likes to speed beyond the legal speed limit is taking an unnecessary risk. Your risk of being injured far outweighs the gain of getting a ride. A **calculated risk** is a chance worth taking after you consider the possible outcomes. Taking a risk in which the possible gain from the action outweighs the possible risk makes sense. Trying out for the school play or a sports team is a calculated risk. If you do not get chosen, you have not lost much. Families can help you see the difference between unnecessary and calculated risks. They can encourage you to take calculated risks that will benefit you, and they will support you if you take a calculated risk and do not get what you wanted.

To learn and practice skills you can use in future relationships

Family life is a healthful, safe place to build your relationship skills. You can learn how to become close to other people. You learn to express love, anger, sadness, and fear, and to resolve conflicts in healthful ways. You learn about your gender role by observing your parents or guardian. Your **gender role**, also referred to as your sex role, is the actions, feelings, and attitudes you have because you are male or female. You can use the skills you learn with your family in future relationships.

Following Family Guidelines

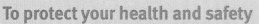

Your parents or guardian show their love for you in two very important ways. They treat you with affection, and they take responsible actions concerning your welfare. Parents and guardians may express their affection by saying that they love you or by giving you a hug. One way they take responsible actions is by providing family guidelines. **Family guidelines** are rules set by your parents or guardian that help you know how to act in various situations. There are important reasons to follow family guidelines.

To protect your health and safety

Your parents or guardian make rules to protect your health and safety. They protect your health by setting rules against smoking, drinking alcohol, taking drugs, and being sexually active. Your safety is their reason for expecting you to stay away from gangs and to be home by a certain hour. They set rules to prevent injury, such as guidelines about traffic safety.

To follow rules and laws

Rules and laws protect society. They allow society to count on its members to behave in certain ways. For example, people can drive at the legal speed limit in opposite directions on a highway separated only by a painted line because people agree to follow traffic laws. Parents and guardians help you follow the rules that will keep you safe. They expect you to follow safety rules in sports. Your parents or guardian also expect you to obey laws. They expect you to not steal or destroy property. Family guidelines can help you follow the rules and laws that protect you and society.

To show respect for yourself and others

Your parents or guardian want you to have self-respect and show respect for others. They expect you to show respect for them and for yourself. For example, they expect you to tell them if someone abuses you. Some of their rules teach you how to show respect for others. For example, perhaps they do not allow you to interrupt other family members when they are talking. Perhaps they expect you to stand if an older person such as a grandparent needs a chair. The habits you form about having and showing respect in your family will help you throughout life.

To show good character

Your parents or guardian know the responsible values that make up good character. They set rules in order to teach you to act on those values. They know that having good character provides you with benefits that can help you succeed all through your life. For example, perhaps they do not allow you to go out on school nights or do not allow you to watch television shows that feature violence. They may tell you to avoid gangs or peers who might encourage risk behaviors. Family guidelines such as these are made to keep you from being influenced in harmful ways.

Family Changes

Changes might occur in a family. These changes might be expected or unexpected. Several common life events change the makeup of the family or the nearness of its members. These life events include

- the birth or adoption of a family member.
- the separation, divorce, or remarriage of parents.
- an illness or injury of a family member.
- a member having to serve in the military, work away from home, or attend college.
- the death of a family member.

Birth and Adoption

The birth of a baby or the adoption of a family member is a time of many changes. These changes may include a new household schedule and added responsibilities. When a baby or younger child joins the family, parents will have less time for their older children. By expressing their feelings, family members can address their own needs for attention and discuss how to meet the needs of the new family member.

Separation, Divorce, and Remarriage

Problems occur from time to time in most marriages. Often couples can work together to solve the problems. Some couples decide to live apart. **Marital separation** is an agreement between a married couple to live apart but remain married. If the husband and wife are unable to resolve their conflicts, they may divorce. **Divorce** is the legal end to a marriage. Divorce often causes stress for family members.

Divorce affects teens in various ways, but divorce always results in change. Some teens are relieved. If a parent was abusive or had a drinking problem, life at home will probably be calmer as a result of the divorce. For many teens, divorce is upsetting. Many teens are surprised to learn that their parents are getting divorced. Some reactions of teens to divorce might include feeling insecure, feeling worried about the future, and feeling angry.

In addition, some teens feel responsible when parents divorce. They believe their actions were part of the cause. They wish they had said or done something differently. Teens may be unsure about what to expect as a result of the divorce. They are afraid they might have to move or go to a different school. They may spend little time with one or both parents. After divorce, one or both parents might date. Teens might resent the time a parent spends dating. They might resent the person the parent is dating.

Parents who divorce might remarry. A **remarriage** is a marriage in which a person who was married before marries again. When children are involved, remarriage forms a blended family. A **blended family** is a family that consists of marriage partners, their children from their previous marriages, and any children they have together. Teens who live in blended families must adjust to the new family situation.

Illness and Injury

When a member of the family contracts a serious illness or has a serious injury, all family members are affected. Worry about the ill or injured person is an ongoing cause of stress. If the family member is in a hospital or other health care facility, time that would be spent in other ways must then be spent on going to the hospital to visit the family member. If the family member is at home but confined to bed, there are new family responsibilities. The family member's condition may require that the usual household noise level be reduced. Teens may have to help out more and change their habits. The family member's illness or injury may result in both loss of income and large medical bills. Family members may have to put off planned purchases.

Military Service, Work, and College

If one or both parents or guardians are called away to perform military service or to fulfill a work assignment away from home, adjustments must be made. The same is true if an older sibling goes away to military service, work, or college. Household chores will have to be redistributed. Teens may have to help out more. They may be asked to take on new responsibilities. Family members will miss the member who must be away. Sometimes they may feel resentment that the person is not there when they need or want him or her so much.

Death of a Family Member

All families eventually experience the death of a family member. The death of an elderly family member is sad, but it is not completely unexpected. The premature death of a family member is usually very stressful. A **premature death** is a death that occurs before a person reaches his or her life expectancy age. A parent or guardian might die. A family member might die as a child or teen. Family members need one another's support when there is a death in the family. Each family member may grieve in his or her own way. It's important to talk about feelings with one another.

If Changes Occur in Your Family

Protect your health.

Family changes can cause stress. **Stress** is the response of the body to the demands of daily living. Stress can increase heart rate and raise blood pressure. Stress can make it difficult to concentrate and to sleep. Stress can lower your resistance to disease. You may be more likely to catch a cold or the flu.

When there is a change in your family, take steps to stay healthy. Have a plan to manage stress.

- Identify the signs of stress.
- Identify the cause of stress.
- Do something about the cause of the stress.

Sometimes you cannot avoid the cause of stress, but try to talk things out with responsible adults who can offer support.

- Reduce the harmful effects of stress. For example,
  - Get plenty of rest and sleep.
  - Eat a balanced diet of healthful foods.
  - Get plenty of exercise.

Express your feelings in healthful ways.

Family changes evoke many different feelings. Changes might cause sadness, anger, insecurity, and fear. It is okay to have these feelings, but to keep them from causing harm, you must express them in healthful ways.

- Share feelings with family members.
- Write about your feelings in a notebook or a letter to yourself.

Adjust to changes.

Family changes affect the routine of every family member. Ways of doing things that you are comfortable with may need to change.

- Ask questions to be sure of what is expected of you.
- Get details about how your routine might change.
- Offer to help other family members change their routines.
- Ask for help if you feel overwhelmed.

Improving Difficult Family Relationships

Some teens live in dysfunctional families. A **dysfunctional family** is a family in which some or all members behave in ways that are not responsible, emotionally healthy, or loving. Family members do not communicate well. They may not express much affection for one another. Perhaps they do not treat one another with respect. Relationships in a dysfunctional family are often difficult. Some causes of difficult family relationships are the following:

1. **Drug Dependence** **Drug dependence** is the continued need for the effects of a drug even though those effects harm the body, mind, and relationships. Drug dependence is also called chemical dependence or addiction.

2. **Other Addictions** An **addiction** is a compelling need to continue a harmful behavior. Workaholism is the compelling need to work. Workaholism, shopping addiction, television addiction, and gambling addiction are some examples of behaviors that can cause difficult family relationships.

3. **Abuse** **Abuse** is the harmful treatment of another person. Abuse may be physical, emotional, or sexual. Chapter 2 discusses types of abuse.

4. **Violence** **Violence** is the use of threats and physical force with the purpose of causing harm. **Domestic violence** is violence that occurs within a family.

5. **Abandonment** **Abandonment** is removing oneself and withdrawing one's protection, support, and help. Parents and guardians who abandon their children often cause physical and emotional hardship to the children.

Steps to Take

If you are experiencing difficult family relationships, here are some steps you can take to improve the relationships.

- **Keep notes of any difficult situations.** Write the date and time. Describe the difficult family situation. Tell how the situation affects you and others. Tell how you feel about it.

- **Talk to a responsible adult family member.** If there is no adult family member with whom you can speak, talk to another adult. Be honest. Share the notes you took. Talk about the difficult family situation. Tell how it affects you. Ask for help if you need it.

- **Participate in a recovery program.** A **recovery program** is a group that provides support to members who want to change their behavior. There are recovery programs for family members who have addictions. There are also support programs for the other family members.

1. **My parents just adopted a 10-year-old girl. Until now I was the only child. Now I am an older brother. My new sister is always getting her way. I don't argue with her when she gets her way, but what can I do?**

   Try talking to your parents about how you feel. However, start with some real observations. Just when and why did your sister "get her way" the last time? Write down your ideas. Think through what you wrote. Are you being fair and respectful? If so, then share your ideas with your parents.

2. **I live with both my parents and my two sisters. My friend lives with only her mother. Is that still considered a family?**

   Yes, there are many combinations that make up a family. You live in a traditional family, *which consists of a husband, wife, and children. Your friend lives in a* single-parent family, *with one parent and one or more children. Here are some other combinations: a* couple *is a family that consists of a husband and wife who have no children. A* foster family *consists of one or more adults caring for a child or children who do not live with their birth parents. A* joint-custody family *consists of two parents who separately spend time with their children and do not live together. A* blended family *consists of two marriage partners, their children from their previous marriages, and any children they have together. An* extended family *includes family members from three or more generations, or age groups, living together.*

3. **My new stepdad has two children from his first marriage. We are all trying to fit in with one another. I have been told that I should take a more proactive approach. What does *proactive* mean?**

   Proactive means anticipating problems and taking actions to head them off. People who have a proactive decision-making style make their own decisions and take responsibility for the consequences. For example, offering to help one of your new siblings with a chore instead of waiting to be told to help may ward off feelings of resentment from the new sibling.

4. **I know that my parents and my peers are two influences on my decisions. Is one of these more important than the other?**

   More often than not, parents are the more important influence. Your parents are responsible for you. They can share with you a richness of family values, traditions, and culture. They may offer a depth of affection and support that your friends may not be able to offer. However, your friends can support you to practice healthful behaviors and develop your talents.

5. **What are some signs that a family member might be grieving over the death of another family member? How might family members support each other after the death of a loved one?**

   There are many ways in which family members might show grief. A family member might refuse to accept the death of the loved one. He or she might be angry or depressed, or become withdrawn. He or she may try to keep very busy. The family member might even participate in risky or self-destructive behavior. Family members need to support one another during these sad times. It is important for all family members to talk about their feelings with one another. Each family member will need time and understanding to deal with grief in his or her own way. In some cases, family members might want to talk to a grief counselor.

6. **What is a *stepfamily*?**

   Stepfamily is a term sometimes used to describe a blended family. A stepfamily consists of a husband, wife, children from both previous marriages, and possibly children the husband and wife have together.

Use Vocabulary

Complete each sentence by choosing the term from the list below that best fits in the blank. Write your answers on a separate sheet of paper.

addiction	dysfunctional family	unnecessary risk
calculated risk	marital separation	

1. A chance worth taking after you consider the possible outcomes is a(n) _____?_____ .

2. A chance not worth taking after you consider the possible outcomes is a(n) _____?_____ .

3. A family in which some or all members behave in ways that are not responsible, emotionally healthy, or loving is a(n) ____?____ .

4. An agreement between a married couple to live apart but remain married is called _____?_____ .

5. A compelling need to continue a harmful behavior is called a(n) _____?_____ .

Review Concepts

Write your answers to the following questions on a separate sheet of paper.

6. Why is it best to have family members, not your peers, fulfill your need to belong?

7. How can family members help you take calculated risks?

8. What are two ways your parents or guardian show that they love you?

9. Why do you need to follow family guidelines?

10. What changes might occur in a family?

11. How can you protect your health if changes occur in your family?

12. What are healthful ways to express feelings if changes occur in your family?

13. How can you adjust if changes occur in your family?

14. What are five causes of difficult family relationships?

15. What are three steps to take if you have difficult family relationships?

Critical Thinking/Problem Solving

Write your responses to the following questions and statements on a separate sheet of paper.

16. Why is it important to make family life a priority?

17. What adjustments might a family need to make if a grandparent who is ill comes to live with them?

Practice Life Skills

18. **Make Responsible Decisions** You have learned about taking unnecessary risks and calculated risks. Make a list of some calculated risks that you think teens might take with the support of family members. Give reasons to explain why the risks are calculated rather than unnecessary.

You will learn...

- **differences in growth patterns among adolescents, such as onset of puberty, and how they may affect personal health.**

- **physical and emotional development during adolescence.**

- **habits that protect male reproductive health.**

- **habits that protect female reproductive health.**

- **what happens during the menstrual cycle.**

Body Changes

Adolescence is the physical, emotional, and social transition from childhood to adulthood. The beginning of adolescence is usually associated with the beginning of puberty. Puberty (PYOO•buhr•tee) is the stage of growth and development when the body becomes capable of producing offspring. Secondary sex characteristics are physical and emotional changes that occur during puberty.

This chapter teaches you about body changes. You can show respect for the male body and the female body by using the appropriate words to refer to them. You can protect reproductive health by practicing specific healthful behaviors.

VOCABULARY*

- adolescence, 37
- puberty, 37
- secondary sex characteristics, 37
- hormone, 38
- testosterone, 38
- estrogen, 38
- mood swings, 38
- body image, 39
- male reproductive system, 40
- sperm, 40

- ejaculation, 40
- semen, 40
- impotence, 41
- erection, 41
- testicular self-examination (TSE), 41
- smegma, 41
- circumcision, 41
- female reproductive system, 42
- menstrual cycle, 43
- ovulation, 43

- menstruation, 43
- follicle, 43
- corpus luteum, 43
- progesterone, 43
- toxic shock syndrome (TSS), 44
- breast self-examination (BSE), 45
- Pap smear, 45
- premenstrual syndrome (PMS), 46

* The names of reproductive organs are listed on page 47.

Changes That Occur During Puberty

Although all adolescents go through the changes of puberty, not all experience these changes at the same time, at the same rate, or in the same way. For some teens, the changes of adolescence happen quickly. Other teens may find that changes come more slowly. You will grow and mature at your own rate during adolescence.

Hormones cause the changes that occur during puberty. A **hormone** is a chemical messenger that is released directly into the bloodstream. The male body secretes the hormone testosterone. **Testosterone** (tes•TAHS•tuh•ROHN) is a hormone that produces male secondary sex characteristics. The female body secretes the hormone estrogen. **Estrogen** (ES•truh•juhn) is a hormone that produces secondary sex characteristics and affects menstruation.

Puberty usually starts between the ages of 8 and 13 in females and 9 and 14 in males. While puberty is marked by periods of great physical growth, it is not just a physical event. The changes that take place during puberty are also emotional, mental or intellectual, and social. All of these changes affect your relationships.

Mood Swings

Mood swings are emotional ups and downs caused by changing hormone levels. Part of becoming more adult is learning how to handle emotional ups and downs. People are accountable for the ways they express emotions. Think about how you can express your emotions in healthful ways.

Secondary Sex Characteristics

Secondary sex characteristics develop during puberty. Some characteristics appear only in males or females; other characteristics appear in both males and females.

MALE SECONDARY SEX CHARACTERISTICS

Increase in height
Increase in perspiration
Growth of facial hair
Growth of underarm hair
Growth of pubic hair
Broadening of shoulders
Deepening of voice
Increase in size of reproductive organs
Increase in muscle mass
Formation of sperm

FEMALE SECONDARY SEX CHARACTERISTICS

Increase in height
Increase in perspiration
Growth of underarm hair
Growth of pubic hair
Increase in breast size
Widening of hips
Increase in size of reproductive organs
Beginning of menstruation
Formation of mature ova

Body Image

The physical changes of puberty can affect a teen's body image. **Body image** is the perception a person has of his or her body. Some teens have difficulty accepting the body changes that occur in adolescence. They may wonder if their development is normal. They may compare their bodies to that of a movie personality or athlete and find that they do not measure up.

Accepting body changes helps teens maintain a positive body image. Teens who have a positive body image are comfortable with the way they look. They do not compare themselves to others. Having a positive body image is essential for good health and healthful relationships.

The Male Reproductive System

The male reproductive system consists of the organs in the male body that are involved in producing offspring. The function of a male's reproductive system is to produce, store, and help move sperm out of the body. Sperm are male reproductive cells. When joined with the female's egg cells, they produce new life. Males begin to make sperm between the ages of 12 and 15.

Ejaculation is the passage of semen from the penis. Ejaculation is the result of a series of muscular contractions. Semen is a mixture of sperm and fluids from the seminal vesicles, prostate gland, and Cowper's glands. During puberty, a male might have "wet dreams." He might ejaculate semen during sleep. This is a normal part of puberty.

Parts of the Male Reproductive System

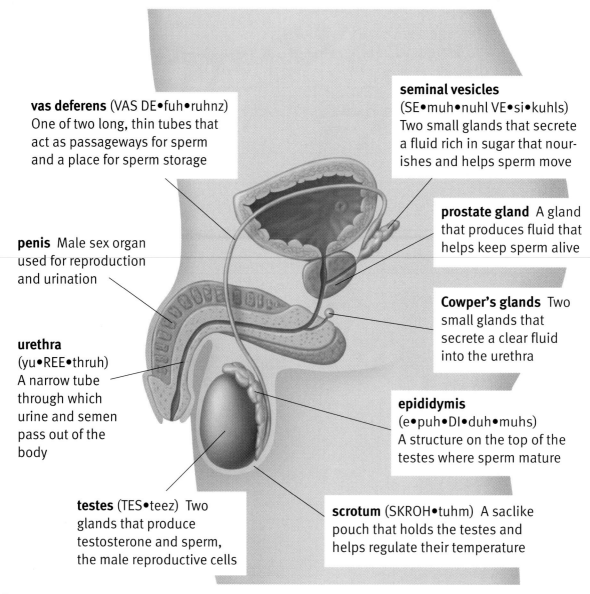

vas deferens (VAS DE•fuh•ruhnz) One of two long, thin tubes that act as passageways for sperm and a place for sperm storage

seminal vesicles (SE•muh•nuhl VE•si•kuhls) Two small glands that secrete a fluid rich in sugar that nourishes and helps sperm move

prostate gland A gland that produces fluid that helps keep sperm alive

penis Male sex organ used for reproduction and urination

Cowper's glands Two small glands that secrete a clear fluid into the urethra

urethra (yu•REE•thruh) A narrow tube through which urine and semen pass out of the body

epididymis (e•puh•DI•duh•muhs) A structure on the top of the testes where sperm mature

testes (TES•teez) Two glands that produce testosterone and sperm, the male reproductive cells

scrotum (SKROH•tuhm) A saclike pouch that holds the testes and helps regulate their temperature

Protecting the Male Reproductive System

A male can practice habits to protect his reproductive health.

- **Practice abstinence from sex until marriage.** Abstinence from sex is choosing not to be sexually active. Practicing abstinence reduces the risk of infection with HIV and sexually transmitted diseases (STDs). HIV is the pathogen that causes AIDS. Several STDs cause a male to be infertile. To be infertile is to be incapable of producing offspring.

- **Do not smoke.** The health habits males have in their teens can affect their ability to have sex when they are married adults. Research shows that smoking harms the arteries that bring blood to the penis. This can result in impotence. **Impotence** is the inability to get and keep an erection. An **erection** is a process that occurs when the penis swells with blood and elongates. Smoking also changes the number, shape, and quality of a male's sperm.

- **Perform TSE.** A **testicular self-examination (TSE)** is a check for lumps and tenderness in the testes. See the box below for instructions on how to perform a TSE.

- **Bathe or shower daily.** Keep the reproductive organs clean. For example, the foreskin needs to be cleaned. The foreskin is a piece of skin that covers the end of the penis. **Smegma** (SMEG•muh) is dead skin and secretions that collect under the foreskin. **Circumcision** (SUHR•kuhm•SI•zhun) is the surgical removal of the foreskin. Many teens had their foreskin removed when they were infants.

- **Have regular medical checkups.** A physician can examine a male and answer any questions he has.

- **Get medical attention for signs of infection.** Lumps, sores, rashes, itching, painful urination, or a discharge from the penis require medical attention. These are symptoms of infection or maybe an STD.

- **Wear an athletic supporter and protective cup for sports.** An athletic supporter supports the penis and testes. A protective cup prevents injuries to these organs.

Testicular Self-Examination (TSE)

Testicular cancer is the leading cause of cancer deaths among males ages 15 to 35. Check for changes and lumps once a month.

1. The best time to examine the testicles is after a shower or bath, when the scrotum is relaxed.

2. Roll each testicle around gently between the thumb and fingers of both hands. Check for any changes, swelling, or lumps.

3. If you find any lump or unusual feeling, tell your parents or guardian and report it to your physician.

The Female Reproductive System

The **female reproductive system** consists of the organs in the female body that are involved in producing offspring. The internal female reproductive organs are the ovaries, fallopian tubes, uterus, cervix, and vagina.

The female's reproductive system has three functions.

1. It produces and stores female reproductive cells, or egg cells. When an egg cell is united with a male's sperm, a new life is produced.

2. It provides a place for a fertilized egg to be nurtured and grow into a baby.

3. It is structured to allow a female to give birth to a baby.

A female is born with about a million immature ova in her ovaries, but they do not start to be released until she reaches puberty. The onset of a female's menstrual cycle generally occurs between the ages of 10 and 15.

Parts of the Female Reproductive System

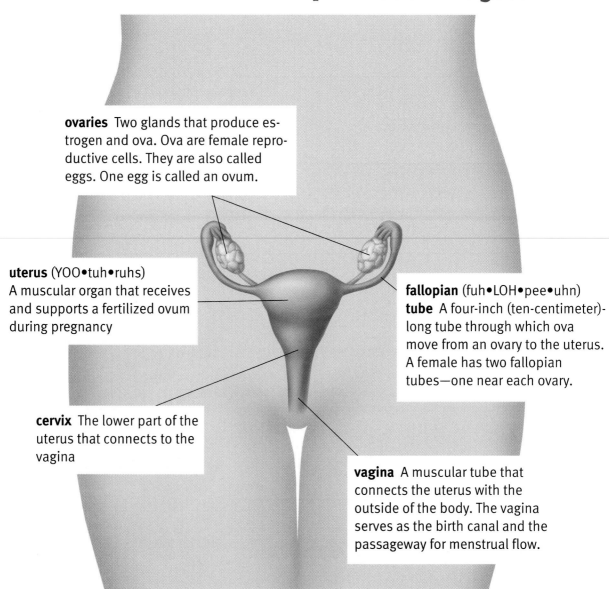

ovaries Two glands that produce estrogen and ova. Ova are female reproductive cells. They are also called eggs. One egg is called an ovum.

uterus (YOO•tuh•ruhs) A muscular organ that receives and supports a fertilized ovum during pregnancy

fallopian (fuh•LOH•pee•uhn) **tube** A four-inch (ten-centimeter)-long tube through which ova move from an ovary to the uterus. A female has two fallopian tubes—one near each ovary.

cervix The lower part of the uterus that connects to the vagina

vagina A muscular tube that connects the uterus with the outside of the body. The vagina serves as the birth canal and the passageway for menstrual flow.

The Menstrual Cycle

The **menstrual cycle** is a monthly cycle that involves ovulation, changes in the uterine lining, and menstruation. **Ovulation** (ahv•you•LAY•shuhn) is the release of a mature ovum from an ovary. **Menstruation** (men•stroo•WAY•shuhn) is the "period," or time during which the menstrual flow leaves the body. The menstrual flow is made up of the unfertilized ovum or egg and the bloody lining of the uterus. The menstrual cycle usually lasts 28 days. This means that there are about 28 days between the first day of one period and the first day of the next period. The menstrual flow usually lasts about five days. Most teens have irregular menstrual cycles. That means that the length of their menstrual cycle and their menstrual flow change from month to month. But it gradually becomes more regular, in most cases, with age.

DAYS 1–4

- Menstruation, or the "period," begins. The menstrual flow leaves the body.
- About 15–20 follicles in the ovary begin to grow. A **follicle** is a pouch that holds an ovum.

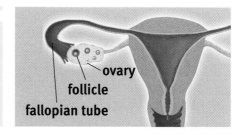

ovary
follicle
fallopian tube

DAYS 5–13

- The growing follicles secrete estrogen. Estrogen causes the lining of the uterus to thicken. Estrogen causes the ova in the follicles to mature.

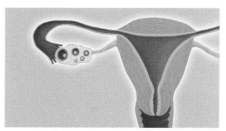

DAY 14

- Ovulation occurs. One of the follicles in the ovary releases a mature ovum into the fallopian tube.
- The ovum begins to travel down the fallopian tube toward the uterus.

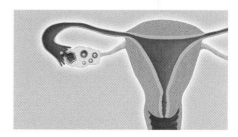

DAYS 15–20

- The follicle that released the ovum becomes a gland called the corpus luteum. The **corpus luteum** (KOR•puhs LOO•tee•uhm) is a temporary gland that secretes progesterone.
- **Progesterone** (proh•JES•tuh•rohn) is a hormone that increases blood flow to the lining of the uterus. This makes the inner uterine lining thicker.

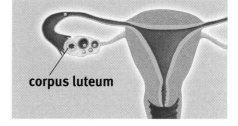

corpus luteum

DAYS 21–28

- The corpus luteum breaks down if the ovum is not fertilized. Progesterone no longer is secreted.
- The bloody lining begins to break away from the uterus.
- This returns the menstrual cycle to Day 1, when the menstrual flow begins.

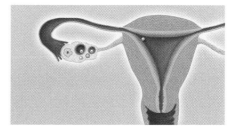

Protecting the Female Reproductive System

A female can practice habits to protect her reproductive health.

- **Practice abstinence from sex until marriage.** Abstinence from sex is choosing not to be sexually active. Practicing abstinence reduces the risk of infection with STDs, and HIV. HIV is the pathogen that causes AIDS. Several STDs can reduce fertility or cause a female to be infertile. To be infertile is to be incapable of producing offspring.

- **Do not smoke.** Research shows that smoking harms the arteries that bring blood to the reproductive organs. Smoking may also cause cancer to reproductive organs such as the cervix.

- **Change pads, panty shields, and tampons often.** These products are used to collect the menstrual flow. A pad should be changed every four to six hours. A panty shield can be used when the menstrual flow is light. It also might be used with a tampon for extra protection. A tampon is a small tube of cotton placed inside the vagina to absorb the menstrual flow. The tampon collects the menstrual flow before it leaves the body. A female can swim and no menstrual flow will get into the water. A tampon must be changed at least every four to six hours.

- **Get prompt medical attention for symptoms of toxic shock syndrome.** **Toxic shock syndrome (TSS)** is a severe illness resulting from toxins secreted by *Staphylococcus* bacteria. Females who use superabsorbent tampons during their periods are at increased risk for TSS. TSS is one reason why females should change tampons often and use the lowest-absorbency tampon that meets their needs. Symptoms of TSS are similar to those of flu: high fever, vomiting, diarrhea, fainting, and skin rash.

- **Keep track of the menstrual cycle on a calendar.** Keep track of the number of days in each menstrual cycle. Keep track of the number of days in the menstrual flow. Make note of menstrual cramps or mood swings that occur. Share the calendar with your parents or guardian and physician.

Breast Self-Examination (BSE)

Females should perform breast self-examination (BSE) each month after the menstrual flow has stopped. This can be done while standing up or lying down. To perform a breast self-exam, do the following:

1. Press the breast firmly with the pads of your fingers. Move the pads of your right fingers over your left breast in small circles, feeling for lumps.

2. Check the right breast with the left hand in the same way.

3. If you feel any lumps, knots, or other changes such as a change in the shape or contour of a breast, tell your parents or guardian and physician right away.

- **Limit caffeine and sodium and get plenty of physical activity.** These habits lessen the likelihood of having menstrual cramps. Menstrual cramps are painful cramps that occur during menstruation. Check with your parents or guardian and physician about medications to relieve pain.

- **Perform BSE each month.** A breast self-examination (BSE) is a monthly check for lumps and changes in the breast. See the box below for instructions on how to perform a BSE.

- **Have regular medical checkups.** A physician can examine a female and discuss body changes. The physician can speak with the teen's parents or guardian about when she should have a pelvic exam and Pap smear. A Pap smear is a screening test for cancer of the cervix.

- **Get medical attention for signs of infections or missed periods.** A discharge from the vagina, lumps, sores, and rashes require medical attention. These are symptoms of some STDs. Missed periods can indicate that a female is pregnant.

Q&A

1. **What is PMS?**

   Premenstrual syndrome (PMS) *is a group of changes that can affect a female before her menstrual period. Some of these changes include headache, backache, tenderness of the breasts, a bloated feeling, weight gain, quick mood changes, and depression. The exact cause of PMS is unknown, but it is believed to result from hormonal changes.*

2. **Is there anything I can do about PMS?**

   You may not be able to eliminate all the discomforts of PMS, but you can reduce the symptoms. You can decrease or eliminate caffeine in your diet. You can reduce the amount of salt in your diet. This will lower the amount of water your body retains. A physician might recommend medication to relieve your symptoms.

3. **I'm only 13 years old, but I've grown almost 4 inches in the past few months. I'm almost 6 feet tall! I tower over my friends. I feel awkward and self-conscious about this. What can I do? Is this normal?**

   What you are experiencing is normal. Teens go through puberty at different rates. A male begins going through puberty at anywhere from 9 to 14 years old. So friends your own age may be in different stages of development. Your friends will catch up with you soon. If you feel stressed and confused about these changes, you may need to talk to your parent or guardian, or another responsible adult.

4. **What causes a male teen's voice to "crack?"**

   At puberty, the size of a male's larynx, or voice box, increases and his voice begins to deepen. While this is happening, his voice may crack, or switch suddenly from a low pitch to a high pitch.

5. **My mother has checkups from a gynecologist. What kind of doctor is that?**

   A gynecologist is a physician who specializes in female reproductive health.

6. **Will a female have menstrual periods for the rest of her life?**

   No. Females stop having periods somewhere between the ages of 45 and 55. This is called menopause. Hormonal changes cause ovulation and menstruation to stop gradually. A female is then no longer able to have children.

7. **What is testicular trauma?**

   Testicular trauma is the pain that a male experiences when his testes are hit, kicked, or crushed. This might happen while he is participating in sports. This is why males should wear an athletic supporter and a protective cup when participating in certain sports.

CHAPTER 4 REVIEW

Use Vocabulary

On a separate sheet of paper, write the correct definitions for the following body parts.

MALE REPRODUCTIVE SYSTEM

1. Cowper's glands
2. epididymis
3. prostate gland
4. scrotum
5. seminal vesicles
6. testes
7. urethra
8. vas deferens

FEMALE REPRODUCTIVE SYSTEM

9. cervix
10. fallopian tube
11. ovaries
12. uterus
13. vagina

Review Concepts

Write your answers to the following questions on a separate sheet of paper.

14. What are two ways to show respect for the male and female body?

15. Which hormone produces secondary sex characteristics in the male? In the female?

16. What causes mood swings?

17. What body changes occur in males during puberty?

18. What body changes occur in females during puberty?

19. What are the organs in the male reproductive system?

20. What are seven habits a male should practice to protect his reproductive health?

21. What are the internal organs in the female reproductive system?

22. What changes occur in the menstrual cycle: Days 1–4? Days 5–13? Day 14? Days 15–20? Days 21–28?

23. What are nine habits a female should practice to protect her reproductive health?

Critical Thinking/Problem Solving

Write your responses to the following questions on a separate sheet of paper.

24. Why is it important for teens to have a positive body image?

25. What effects might smoking have on the male and female reproductive systems?

Practice Life Skills

26. **Practice Healthful Behaviors** How does practicing abstinence from sex before marriage protect male and female reproductive health?

5

You will learn...

- why abstinence from sex is the expected standard for you and reasons to practice abstinence from sex.

- the rules and responsibilities of dating.

- guidelines for expressing affection.

- why it is risky to drink alcohol or use other drugs.

- what can happen if you are slipped a drug and how to reduce the risk of being slipped a drug.

- how to choose entertainment that promotes family values.

- resistance skills you can use if you are pressured to be sexually active.

- steps that teens who have been sexually active can take to change their behavior.

Choose Abstinence from Sex

Abstinence from sex is choosing not to be sexually active. When you choose abstinence from sex, you make a responsible decision. You delay gratification and wait until you are a married adult to engage in sexual activity. To **delay gratification** is to put off doing something pleasurable until the appropriate time. This chapter explains why practicing abstinence from sex is a responsible decision. Learn skills to support your decision to practice abstinence from sex.

VOCABULARY

- **abstinence from sex,** 49
- **delay gratification,** 49
- **sexual feelings,** 52
- **affection,** 52
- **drug-free lifestyle,** 54
- **drug slipping,** 54
- **rape,** 54
- **family values,** 55
- **faulty thinking,** 55
- **sexual harassment,** 58

Dating

As you move into an exciting time in your life, you want to spend time with members of the opposite gender. Your circle of friendships will expand to include them. You might think about opposite-gender friends and what dating will be like. These normal and healthful feelings are important to you, but they come with new responsibilities to yourself and others.

You will want to learn how to deal with new and often powerful feelings. You will want to learn how to show your own good character traits and practice the values of your family. You will want to learn to act in ways that show you can manage your social life.

Group Dating

Many teens begin dating by going out in groups. Group dating is a way to practice your social skills. You probably have common interests with your friends. Group dating with friends is a fun and less stressful way to learn about others. You learn

- what kind of people you enjoy being with most.
- to relax and be yourself with the opposite gender.
- what activities you enjoy doing with another person.
- how other people act in social situations.
- to show someone that he or she is special without taking risks.

As you expand your friendships, you may discover your own ideas about gender roles. In Chapter 3, you learned that a gender role is the way a person acts and the feelings he or she has about being male or female. Most people get their attitudes about gender roles from the adults around them. As you learn more about people, you may find that their ideas about gender roles for males and females are similar to or different from yours. Show respect for both genders by recognizing that males and females deserve equal opportunities. Treat members of both genders with respect.

Group Activities You Can Enjoy

- Play a board game.
- Watch a movie appropriate for your age group.
- Do your homework together.
- Go bike riding, skating, or bowling.
- Play basketball, softball, or soccer.
- Go to an amusement park or swimming pool.
- Go shopping.
- Attend a sports event or concert.
- Do volunteer work.
- Attend a school event such as a play or after-school club meeting.

Individual Dating

Eventually, you will probably want to go on a date with just one person. This is the time for understanding the rules and responsibilities of dating. Talk with your parents or guardian about their expectations. They may want you to be a certain age. They may let you date but will limit places and times. By following the dating guidelines listed below, you can avoid misunderstandings and conflicts.

The Person You Are Dating

Dating is a way to get to know a person. Yet for your own comfort and safety, you need to know some things up front about a person you might date. Here's a checklist of questions. Can you answer "Yes" to all of them?

1. Does the person show a sincere interest in what I say and do?
2. Does the person show respect for me, being kind and considerate to all people in and out of school?
3. Does the person make responsible decisions that are healthful, safe, legal, and respectful of self and others; follow family guidelines; and demonstrate good character?
4. Is the person always nonviolent, avoiding the use of physical force to hurt or tease anyone?

5. Does the person encourage me to do my best in school?
6. Does the person choose friends who are responsible individuals?
7. Does the person have a healthful and respectful attitude toward both males and females?

If you can't answer "Yes" to all of these questions, you would be wise to consider dating someone else. As attractive as someone might seem, a single "No" answer will help you make a responsible decision. Date only someone who has good character.

Dating Guidelines

- Do not date anyone without the approval of your parents or guardian.
- Discuss dating guidelines in advance. How often are you allowed to date? Can you date on school nights or only on weekends? What time must you be home?
- Respect the responsible dating rules of the person with whom you are going to have a date.
- Talk over specific plans with your parents or guardian before you go on a date. Where are you going, and with whom, and what time will you be home? Always let someone at home know if your plans change or if you are delayed.

- Make transportation arrangements clear. How are you going to get where you're going? How are you both getting home? Make sure both sets of parents or guardians know the plans. If one parent or guardian is to provide transportation, make sure that the person is willing and available.
- Carry a cell phone with you, if possible, and keep it turned on so that your parents or guardian can reach you.
- Call your parents or guardian if any situation arises that makes you uncomfortable.

Expressing Affection

During puberty, your body changes. As this happens, you experience powerful new feelings. **Sexual feelings** are feelings that result from attraction to another person. It is normal and okay to have sexual feelings. It is *NOT* okay to be sexually active.

You must set limits for expressing affection. **Affection** is a fond or tender feeling for another person. When you set limits, you stay in control of your feelings. You stick to responsible values. You do not go too far and later regret your actions. It helps to think ahead. Talk to your parents or guardian about ways to express affection without going too far.

Guidelines for Expressing Affection

1. Limit your expressions of affection to hand-holding, hugging, and casual kissing to keep your brain in control of your decisions and actions.
2. Tell a person your limits for expressing affection. Make sure both of you understand what the limits are. Don't be afraid to say "no" clearly and consistently.
3. Do not date someone who does not respect your limits.
4. Do not drink alcohol or use other drugs. They interfere with responsible judgment.
5. Do not date someone who uses alcohol or other drugs.

Appropriate Ways to Express Affection

There are healthful and appropriate ways to express affection. Teens who want to express affection for someone can

- express their feelings in words—through conversation or in notes or cards.
- talk about feelings together.
- take a walk together, hand in hand or arm in arm.
- share a hug.
- make a gift for the other person.
- do something kind for the other person.
- sit together and listen to music or watch a movie appropriate for your age group.
- teach each other something new.
- plan a surprise for the other person.

Affection for another person is a wonderful feeling. However, it is important to find ways to show that you care without putting yourself at risk of going too far.

Abstinence from Sex as the Expected Standard for Teens

The Guidelines for Making Responsible Decisions™ are six questions to ask to make sure a decision is a responsible one. Ask these questions to learn why abstinence from sex is the expected standard for you.

1. Is it healthful for me to practice abstinence from sex?

Practicing abstinence from sex is healthful.

- You reduce the risk of becoming infected with HIV and developing AIDS.
- You reduce the risk of becoming infected with other sexually transmitted diseases (STDs).
- You will not become a teenage parent.

2. Is it safe for me to practice abstinence from sex?

Practicing abstinence from sex is safe.

- You reduce the risk of becoming a victim of rape or assault.
- You reduce the risk of violence that is associated with teen parenthood.

3. Do I follow rules and laws if I practice abstinence from sex?

Practicing abstinence from sex follows rules and laws.

- You avoid being in situations that could lead to being prosecuted for having sex with a minor.
- You avoid sexual behavior for which you can be prosecuted for date rape.

4. Do I show respect for myself and others if I practice abstinence from sex?

Practicing abstinence from sex shows respect for myself and others.

- You do not place yourself or others in risky situations.
- You maintain a good reputation because you are responsible.

5. Do I follow my family's guidelines if I practice abstinence from sex?

Practicing abstinence from sex follows my family's guidelines.

- You avoid conflicts with your parents or guardian because you follow their guidelines.

6. Do I show good character if I practice abstinence from sex?

Practicing abstinence from sex shows good character.

- You delay gratification and wait until you are a married adult to have sex.

Being Drug Free

A **drug-free lifestyle** is a lifestyle in which you do not misuse or abuse drugs. Alcohol and other harmful drugs affect the part of your brain that controls judgment. What are the consequences of drinking alcohol or using other harmful drugs? Your brain will be affected, and you might not even know it. Then you are not really in control of making decisions. You might not stick to your plan to practice abstinence from sex. Then you risk getting pregnant or getting someone pregnant. You risk being infected with HIV and other STDs. You risk becoming drug dependent. If you are drug dependent, you might act in wrong ways to get drugs. You might exchange sex for drugs.

What might happen if you went out with teens who drink alcohol or use other harmful drugs? You would be at risk for being slipped a drug. **Drug slipping** is placing a drug into someone's food or beverage without that person's knowledge. Some drugs used for drug slipping increase the risk of rape. A date rape drug, such as ecstasy, roofies, or GHB, might be slipped into a beverage you are drinking. These drugs can cause you to pass out. After you pass out, a person might have sex with you. When you awaken, you may remember nothing. You are a victim of rape. **Rape** is the threatened or actual use of physical force to have sex with a person who has not given or is not capable of giving consent. Take steps to reduce your risk of being slipped a drug.

Drug Slipping

Here's how to reduce your risk of being slipped a drug.

- Always keep your food or beverage in sight.

- Serve your own food or beverage when possible.

- Do not accept an open beverage container from someone you do not know.

- Do not attend parties or social gatherings where there is drug use.

- Call a parent, guardian, or other responsible adult if you have signs of drug use, such as dizziness or extreme drowsiness.

- Go to an emergency room if you suspect you have been slipped a drug.

- Ask someone to keep a sample of the food or drink as evidence.

Risks of Drinking Alcohol and Using Other Harmful Drugs

1. You might not stick to your decision to practice abstinence from sex.
2. You increase your risk of getting pregnant or getting someone pregnant.
3. You increase the risk of becoming infected with HIV and other STDs.
4. You increase the risk of being in situations in which rape occurs.
5. You are around others who use drugs, and you increase the risk of being slipped a drug.
6. You might become drug dependent and exchange sex for drugs or the money to buy drugs.
7. You might share a needle that has infected blood on it.

Choosing Entertainment

Entertainment is something you do for enjoyment. You might watch TV, DVDs, or videotapes. You might go to movies. You might read books or listen to music. You might access the Internet or play computer games. Ideas and images from entertainment can have a powerful influence on your thoughts and actions. Because of that power, you must make wise choices about entertainment.

Choose entertainment that promotes family values. **Family values** are beliefs that strengthen family bonds. You are less likely to develop faulty thinking when the entertainment you choose promotes family values. **Faulty thinking** is a thought process in which you deny facts or believe wrong ideas.

Suppose you regularly watch a TV sitcom or soap opera. The teens in the show might be sexually active. Suppose an unmarried teen character on the show has a baby. After the baby is born, the teen mother still sees her friends. The baby's father continues to see the baby and the baby's mother. Financial problems don't appear. Such a sitcom or soap opera is far from reality. It does not show friends dropping away, the burden of money problems, or the never-ending daily work that having a baby brings. There are no consequences to the behavior.

Suppose you watch crime dramas or play video games that show females being sexually harassed or molested. You might become *desensitized* to violence against females. This means that by being exposed to it, you no longer think that it is wrong. Such entertainment sometimes makes the crimes seem glamorous or exciting. Without realizing it, you may come to assume that these assaults are normal. You may begin to think of women in these terms.

These forms of entertainment send wrong or faulty messages. The images of these wrong messages can be hard to shake. They can affect your thought processes and lead you to faulty thinking. You may come to think it is okay to act as these characters do. If you do, you will be denying facts. It is not okay.

Entertainment is not the same as real life. Sexual activity has serious consequences. Real people face real problems as a result. Life is difficult for teen parents and babies born to teen parents. Survivors of sexual crimes endure pain for years.

Entertainment That Promotes Family Values:

- Is approved for your age group.
- Is approved by your parents, guardian, or another responsible adult.
- Does not show harmful drug use as acceptable behavior.
- Does not show sex outside of marriage as acceptable behavior.
- Does not show violence or sexual assault as acceptable behavior.

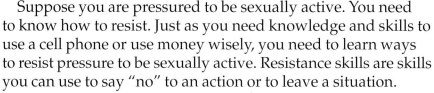

Using Resistance Skills

Suppose you are pressured to be sexually active. You need to know how to resist. Just as you need knowledge and skills to use a cell phone or use money wisely, you need to learn ways to resist pressure to be sexually active. Resistance skills are skills you can use to say "no" to an action or to leave a situation.

1. **Say "no" in a firm voice.** Look directly at the person who is pressuring you and show confidence. Make your limits clear. Do not apologize for saying "no." You can be proud of your choice.

2. **Give reasons for practicing abstinence.** There are good reasons for you to say "no." Use the list on the next page.

3. **Repeat your reasons for practicing abstinence.** Get your message across, and do not get drawn into discussions about whether your reasons are good. They are.

4. **Don't send a mixed message.** Make sure your actions match your words. Do not tease someone in a sexual way, or act as if you are willing to be sexually active. All your behavior must support your "no."

5. **Avoid situations in which there will be pressure to be sexually active.** The easiest way to escape pressure is not to face it in the first place. Do not go to parties that are not supervised by adults. Do not go to a person's home if you do not have the approval of a parent or guardian. Do not go to the bedroom of a teen of the opposite sex. Do not go to secluded places. If you do find yourself in an uncomfortable or unsafe place, leave.

6. **Break off a relationship when someone does not respect your limits.** Suppose someone continues to pressure you after you have said "no." This person is not showing respect for you. Tell your parents or guardian about the pressure you are getting. Ask for their support.

7. **Influence others to practice abstinence.** Other teens respect you when you influence them to practice abstinence. They know you support their family's guidelines. They know you want them to stay healthy. They know you want them to keep a good reputation. You show that you care when you influence others to do what is best.

It's Never Too Late to Practice Abstinence from Sex

Most teens are not sexually active. Teens who have been sexually active can take steps to change their behavior. They can

- **tell their parents or guardian.** Doing so will take some courage. Their parents or guardian will be disappointed that their guidelines were not followed. They will probably be angry, too. They might consider appropriate punishment for breaking guidelines. Still, teens should tell their parents or guardian if they have been sexually active.

- **have a medical checkup.** Teens who have been sexually active might be infected with STDs, including HIV. They might need to be treated. They might need to see a physician or go to a clinic to have a test done to determine if they are infected. They might need to tell a partner to get treatment. Females who have been sexually active might be pregnant.

- **choose behaviors that support the decision to practice abstinence from sex.** Teens who have been sexually active should avoid being with anyone who presses for sexual activity. They should stay away from teens who think it is okay to be sexually active. They should stay drug free and choose friends who are drug free. They should choose entertainment that promotes family values. They should spend more time with family members and those who support their decision to practice abstinence.

The Top Ten List of Reasons to Practice Abstinence

1. I want to follow family guidelines.
2. I want to respect myself.
3. I want to respect others.
4. I want to have a good reputation.
5. I don't want to feel guilty.
6. I am not ready for marriage.
7. I do not want to risk pregnancy.
8. I am not ready to be a parent.
9. I do not want to be infected with an STD.
10. I do not want to be infected with HIV.

1. **I have made the decision to practice abstinence until I am married. My friend laughs at me and says it's silly to make such a decision already. She's going to wait until she's faced with the problem and decide what to do then. I say that's too late! Am I right?**

   Yes, you are right. Tell your friend that it's easier for her to decide now about limits on sexual behavior before she finds herself in a situation where sexual feelings build up. Like you, she should have a plan of action now that will help her abstain from sexual activity.

2. **A group of us want to organize an assembly promoting abstinence. Who might be an influential guest speaker?**

   One option is Erika Harold, who was Miss America for the year 2003. She is an advocate for youth and several of the problems they face today. She has traveled thousands of miles across the nation speaking at schools about violence prevention and making healthful choices. Through Illinois's Project Reality program, Erika promotes a platform of abstinence from alcohol, drugs, and sexual activity before marriage. Her lectures to teen audiences are always well received.

3. **I've been invited to a party where I know there won't be any adults. I'm not a child, and I know what I should and shouldn't do. Why shouldn't I join my friends at the party?**

   It's not really a question of what you know. It's a question of what might end up happening. Peer pressure, alcohol or drugs, physical force, or a lapse in judgment could all result in your not sticking to your decision to practice abstinence. Some of those factors at this party simply will not be in your control. It's hard enough to deal with sexual feelings sometimes, so the more factors in the environment that are under control, the better your chances for success.

4. **What is sexual harassment?**

   __Sexual harassment__ refers to unwanted sexual advances that range from making unwanted sexual comments or gestures or attempting to force another person into unwanted sexual activity. Sexual harassment may include physical contact, such as grabbing and pinching, name-calling, sexual teasing or threats, and suggestive phone calls or e-mails. Students who are harassed should tell a responsible adult. Federal law prohibits sexual harassment. Once a sexual harassment complaint is lodged, a school must investigate and take action.

5. **I have already become sexually active. Now that I've started, what difference does it make?**

   It makes a great deal of difference. You should get a medical checkup and take steps to change your behavior. Perhaps you've been lucky so far and have not been harmed, infected with HIV or other pathogens that cause STDs, or become pregnant. That doesn't mean you won't the very next time you engage in sexual activity. There is no guaranteed way to avoid pregnancy or STDs except abstinence, and that can start today. Talk to your parents or guardian, and take the steps listed on page 57 that will protect you and others.

Use Vocabulary

Complete each sentence by choosing the term from the list below that best fits in the blank. Write your answers on a separate sheet of paper.

abstinence from sex	family values	sexual feelings
affection	rape	

1. Feelings that result from an attraction to another person are _____?_____.

2. The threatened or actual use of physical force to get someone to have sex without giving consent is _____?_____.

3. A tender or fond feeling you may have for someone is _____?_____.

4. The only certain protection from pregnancy and STDs is _____?_____.

5. Beliefs that strengthen family bonds are _____?_____.

Review Concepts

Write your answers to the following questions on a separate sheet of paper.

6. Why is abstinence from sex the expected standard for you?

7. What are five guidelines for expressing affection?

8. Why is it risky to drink alcohol or use other drugs?

9. What can happen if you are slipped a drug?

10. How can you reduce the risk of being slipped a drug?

11. Why is it risky to choose entertainment that does not promote family values?

12. How can you choose entertainment that promotes family values?

13. What are the resistance skills to use if you are pressured to be sexually active?

14. What are ten reasons to practice abstinence?

15. Name steps teens who have been sexually active can take to change their behavior.

Critical Thinking/Problem Solving

Write your responses to the following questions and statements on a separate sheet of paper.

16. Explain some of the things you can learn by group dating.

17. What limits do your parents or guardian want you to set for expressing affection?

18. What do your parents or guardian expect you to do if you attend a party and find out that some teens are drinking alcohol?

Practice Life Skills

19. **Analyze What Influences Your Health** Identify three television programs that promote family values. Discuss what these values are. How do these programs show responsible behavior?

6

You will learn...

- the benefits of a monogamous traditional marriage.

- reasons why teen marriage and parenthood are risky.

- reasons why you should be a married adult before you become a parent.

- ways in which the behavior of mothers-to-be and fathers-to-be can affect the health of their baby.

- how an embryo and a fetus develop.

- what happens during childbirth.

- how parents bond with their baby.

Prevent Teen Marriage, Pregnancy, and Parenthood

Marriage is an emotional and legal commitment made by a husband and wife. A **commitment** is a pledge or promise to do something. The emotional commitment is a promise to love one another. It also is the promise to love children in the marriage. The legal commitment is the obligation to provide for people in the marriage. A couple agrees to make money decisions together and to provide for children for whom they are responsible. You are not ready for these commitments right now. This chapter discusses how practicing abstinence from sex prevents teen pregnancy, teen marriage, and teen parenthood. Prepare for the future. Work on skills to use when you are an adult.

VOCABULARY

- **marriage,** 61
- **commitment,** 61
- **self-sufficient,** 62
- **monogamous traditional marriage,** 62
- **anemia,** 65
- **preeclampsia,** 65
- **premature birth,** 65
- **low birth weight,** 65
- **infertile,** 66
- **prenatal care,** 67
- **pregnancy,** 67
- **conception,** 67
- **umbilical cord,** 67
- **placenta,** 67
- **fetal alcohol syndrome (FAS),** 67
- **miscarriage,** 67
- **zygote,** 68
- **embryo,** 68
- **fetus,** 68
- **labor,** 70
- **childbirth,** 70
- **bonding,** 71

What to Know About Marriage

Marriage is intended to be a special relationship—one of total dedication. When a couple marries, partners promise to love and care for one another for the rest of their lives. They make a commitment to making their marriage last. Most couples achieve this goal. You may be surprised to learn that divorce rates have gone down. Most married couples say they are happy and want to stay together.

Ask Yourself

Don't fool yourself. "Forever" is a long time. Think how long ago even 3 or 4 years seems. Now consider 10 or 20 or 40 or 50 years. Are you ready to make a commitment that will last 50 years—or maybe more? A marriage is more likely to be a happy one if each partner can answer "yes" to each of the following questions.

1. **Are we both at least 22 years old?** You increase your chance to stay married if you are at least 22 years old. You will have had time to learn the skills you need. Your marriage is more likely to be happy if you are close in age.

2. **Are we self-sufficient?** To be self-sufficient is to have the skills and money you need to care for yourself. You will have bills to pay. If you become a parent, you will have children to provide for. You need skills for a job. One or both partners need a job to earn money to provide for the family.

3. **Are we best friends?** Your marriage partner must be someone you would choose for a friend. You should have common interests and shared respect. Sharing interests helps guarantee that you will spend time together.

4. **Do we have the same values?** When you have similar beliefs, decision making is easier. You have the same standards.

5. **Are we committed to a monogamous traditional marriage?** A monogamous (muh•NAH•guh•mus) traditional marriage is a marriage in which a husband and wife have sex only with one another.

About Marriage

There are many benefits to a monogamous traditional marriage.

- It protects the marriage commitment.
- It preserves the tradition of marriage.
- It helps prevent divorce.
- It provides emotional security and trust.
- It helps protect marriage partners from infections with HIV and STDs.
- It provides a secure family life for children of the marriage.

Why Teen Marriage Is Risky

It is a fact. Teen marriage is risky. It is far less likely to work out than a marriage that begins later. Teens have strong feelings, but they have not had enough time to learn about themselves, their possibilities, or how the world works. So here is some straight truth.

Teens who marry . . .

- do not have a chance to learn who they are or understand the emotions they feel.
- do not have enough experience to tell the difference between love and sexual attraction.
- miss out on many social activities that other teens get to experience.
- do not have an opportunity to develop their own ideas and value systems.
- miss the chance to meet and develop relationships with a variety of people of the opposite gender.
- find it difficult to achieve financial and emotional independence from parents.
- are less likely to form a support network of reliable friends who can help them through difficult times.
- have a hard time earning enough money to support a family.
- have less time and opportunity to prepare for a career.

When to Become a Parent

Someday you might choose to become a parent. As a parent, you have the opportunity to love and guide a child. You help a child grow and develop. Being a parent is a serious, full-time responsibility.

Just as getting married requires a commitment to a partner, having a baby requires a commitment to a child. There are good reasons to be a married adult before you become a parent.

Married adult parents have a foundation that provides a stable home life for children.

The best situation is for a child to live with two loving, married adult parents. Married adults are more likely to be able to cope with the demands of being a parent. For all its rewards, raising a child is a lot of work. Especially in the first years, children need constant attention and leave little time for much else. Two people who are committed to each other have a better chance of being able to face and share the continuous effort. Children grow up with role models of a loving father and mother.

Married adult parents are more likely to have the financial resources needed to raise a child.

Raising children is expensive. The costs of raising a child begin before the child is born and continue until the child grows up and becomes independent. Consider the costs of having a baby.

- Health and hospital insurance
- Health care for the mother-to-be
- Maternity clothes for the mother-to-be
- Doctor visits—regular baby checkups, immunizations, sick visits, and medicines
- Baby furniture, including crib and chest, bedding, bathtub, stroller, high chair, safety restraints for cars
- Baby clothing and toys
- Baby food and vitamins
- Baby supplies, including diapers, bottles, diaper rash ointments, baby soap and shampoo, baby oil
- Possible need for child care

Married adult parents are more mature and capable of meeting the responsibilities of parenthood.

When you become a parent, you are responsible for raising a child. Whether the child is newborn or adopted, there are certain promises you must keep. These ten promises are listed in *The Parent Pledge to a Child* on page 71. Two married adults are better able to keep these promises.

Why Teen Parenthood Is Risky

Teen parenthood is risky. In Chapter 5, you learned that one cause of faulty thinking is denying facts. Here are some undeniable facts.

Babies Born to Teen Parents

- often do not receive adequate nourishment
- often do not receive adequate prenatal care
- risk being born prematurely and having a low birth weight
- are more likely to be abused or neglected by their parents
- are less likely to have adequate medical and dental care as children

Teen Fathers

- may have to pay child support and be financially stressed
- are more likely to drop out of school because they must get a job
- are less likely to meet their career goals
- are more likely to neglect or abuse their children

Teen Mothers

- risk anemia during pregnancy
- risk preeclampsia
- risk premature birth of their children
- are more likely to drop out of school
- are less likely to meet their career goals
- have limited social opportunities
- are more likely to have a low income
- are more likely to neglect or abuse their children

Risks of Teen Pregnancy

Teen mothers and their babies are more likely to have one or more of the following:

- **Anemia** is a condition in which the oxygen-carrying capacity of the blood is below normal. Anemia can cause serious complications for the developing baby.

- **Preeclampsia** (pre•e•CLAMP•see•a), also called toxemia, is a very serious disorder of pregnancy characterized by high blood pressure, tissue swelling, and protein in the urine. It is potentially fatal for both mother and child.

- A **premature birth** is the birth of a baby before it is fully developed or the birth of a baby less than 38 weeks from the time of conception. Babies born prematurely have more health problems.

- A **low birth weight** is a weight at birth less than 5.5 pounds (2.5 kilograms). Low-birth-weight babies have more health problems.

Pregnancy

You may want to be a parent someday. Are you aware that your behavior right now can affect your child? Gather the facts. Choose behaviors that keep you healthy. Continue these behaviors all your life.

Ways a Male's Health Habits Can Affect His Baby

A male's health habits can affect the number and makeup of his sperm. His health habits might cause him to be infertile. To be **infertile** is to be incapable of producing offspring. His health habits also can affect the health of the mother of his children. Here are some examples.

Drinking alcohol, smoking, or using other drugs

These substances can have adverse effects on the quality of life of those who use them and those around them. One of these effects is that they can cause a male to be infertile.

Smoking around a pregnant female

The mother-to-be and the baby will be affected. The mother-to-be will breathe the toxic chemicals, drugs, and gases. They will enter the bloodstream of the developing baby.

Being exposed to paints, pesticides, and other toxic chemicals

These substances affect the makeup of the sperm. The baby is at risk for some childhood cancers. There is also increased risk for miscarriage and stillbirth. Stillbirth is the birth of a dead baby.

A healthy adult father is more likely to produce a healthy baby. Take care of yourself for your own sake and for the sake of the child you may one day want to have.

Why a Pregnancy Test Is Needed Right Away

A female who thinks she could be pregnant should have a pregnancy test right away. She needs to know if she is pregnant. If she is, she needs prenatal care. **Prenatal care** is care that is given to a mother-to-be and her developing baby. A physician examines the mother-to-be and provides a plan for a healthful pregnancy.

Ways a Female's Health Habits Can Affect Her Baby

Pregnancy is the time between conception and birth. **Conception** is the fertilization of the ovum by the sperm. The mother-to-be and the baby are connected during the first week of pregnancy. The **umbilical cord** is a ropelike cord that connects the developing baby to the placenta. The **placenta** is a structure that attaches the ovum to the inner wall of the uterus. Substances that get into the mother-to-be's body can get into the baby's body through the umbilical cord. The following behaviors are harmful right now and during pregnancy.

Drinking alcohol

Fetal alcohol syndrome (FAS) describes birth defects in a baby born to a mother who drank alcohol during pregnancy. Babies born with FAS may be mentally retarded, have heart disease, or have defects in joints, arms, and legs. Even small amounts of alcohol can damage the developing baby.

Smoking cigarettes

Nicotine is a harmful drug in cigarettes. Active smoking can cause miscarriage, premature birth, low birth weight, respiratory conditions in newborns, and growth restriction. **Miscarriage** is the body's early ending of a pregnancy. Low-birth-weight babies often have physical and mental problems. Smoking cigarettes can also increase the risk of *SIDS—sudden infant death syndrome*—a condition in which a seemingly healthy baby dies for no apparent reason.

Using crack or cocaine

These drugs are illegal and harmful. They also cause miscarriage and premature birth. A baby can be born with brain damage and other birth defects because of a mother-to-be's crack or cocaine use. A baby can be born addicted to these drugs.

Inhaling chemicals and secondhand smoke

The developing baby can be affected by fumes from what the mother-to-be breathes. Inhaling glue can affect the brain of the developing fetus. Inhaling secondhand smoke from cigarettes and cigars can cause miscarriage, premature birth, and low birth weight. Inhaling pesticides can harm the nervous system of the developing baby.

Exposure to infections

Some infections that a pregnant female gets can harm her developing baby. STDs and rubella, also called German measles, are examples. Females should be vaccinated against rubella before becoming pregnant.

As a general rule, if the mother-to-be is exposed to something, so is the developing baby. A developing baby, though, is tiny and far more affected by harmful substances.

The Stages of Development

There are three main terms for humans as they develop inside the female. These terms are based on the length of time from conception. A **zygote** is the single cell formed by conception when a sperm and ovum unite. This cell begins dividing almost immediately. An **embryo** is the name for the cells that form during the first eight weeks after conception. In the uterus, a thin membrane called an amniotic sac surrounds the developing embryo. The sac is filled with fluid, which protects the embryo from injury and ensures a constant temperature. A **fetus** is the name for a developing baby from the eighth week after conception until it is born.

The growth of an embryo and a fetus takes place over a period of about nine months. This time span is broken up into trimesters, each about three months in length.

The First Trimester

During the first trimester, body systems form. By the end of the fourth week, the embryo has a heart, brain, and lungs. Its digestive and nervous systems have also developed, and its eyes and ears are visible. By the end of the eighth week, the developing baby—now called a fetus—has arms, fingers, legs, and toes. A physician may be able to determine the sex of the fetus through a special test called an ultrasound. At the end of the first trimester, the baby weighs about 1.5 ounces and is about 1.5 inches long.

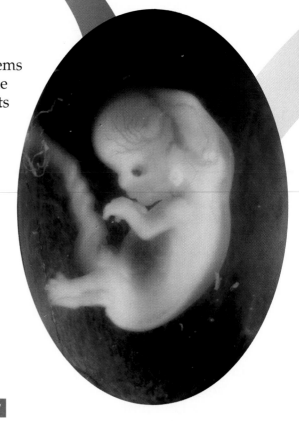

1st Trimester

Month 1   Month 2   Month 3   Month 4

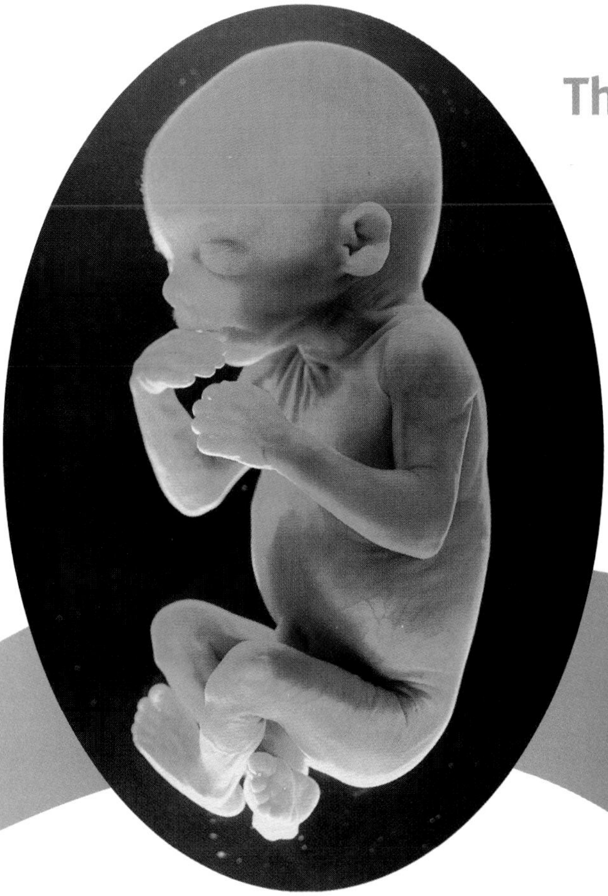

The Second Trimester

During the second trimester, the fetus develops skin. Fine hair, eyelashes, and fingernails appear. By the end of the sixth month, the mother can feel the fetus kick its legs and move its arms within the amniotic sac. Such movement may be a response to pressure or to the developing baby's new ability to hear sounds. The fetus weighs about 1.5 pounds and is about 11.5 to 12.5 inches long.

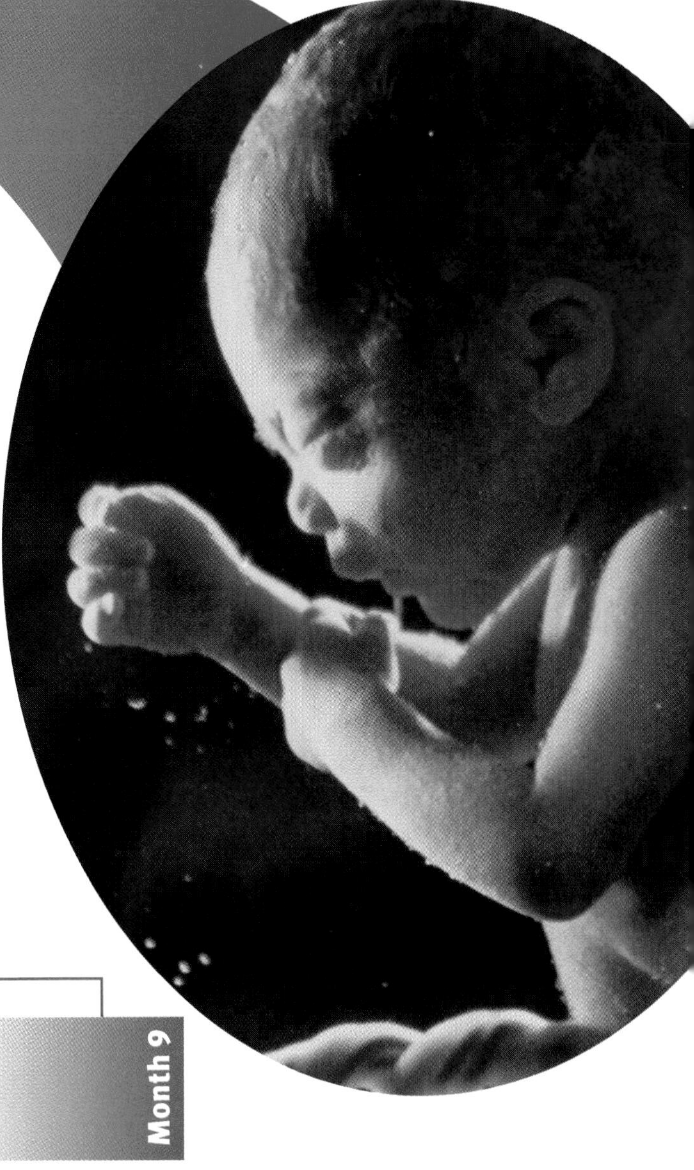

The Third Trimester

During the last trimester, the weight of the fetus more than triples. Its eyes open, its fingers can grasp, and its body organs and systems can work on their own. By the end of the ninth month, the fetus has smooth skin and its eyes are slate-colored. At birth, babies weigh an average of 6 to 9 pounds and are about 19 to 21 inches long.

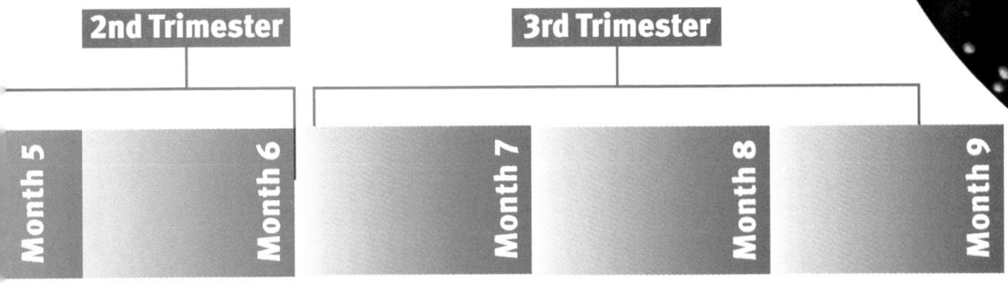

2nd Trimester

3rd Trimester

Month 5

Month 6

Month 7

Month 8

Month 9

What Happens During Childbirth

Labor is a series of changes that result in the birth of a baby. **Childbirth** is the process by which the baby moves from the uterus out of the mother's body. Muscular contractions of the uterus force the baby toward the cervix.

Stage 1
The lower part of the uterus, the cervix, dilates or widens enough for the baby to pass through. This stage can last from two hours to an entire day. The average labor for a first-time mother is about 12 hours. For subsequent births, the time is usually shorter.

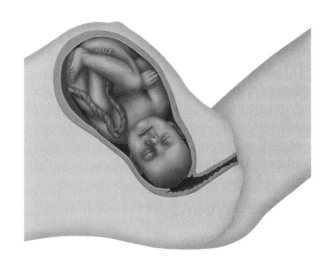

Stage 2
The baby passes into the birth canal, or vagina. The baby passes out of the birth canal and begins to breathe on its own. The umbilical cord is cut.

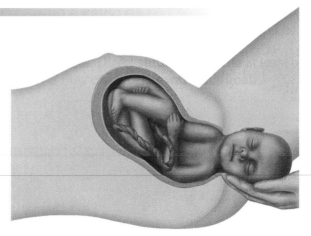

Stage 3
The placenta passes out of the birth canal. If this stage does not occur, the physician removes the placenta.

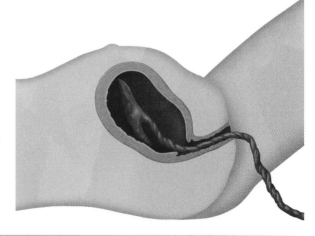

Qualities of Responsible Parents

Responsible parents put raising their children first in their lives. They pledge or promise to make their actions responsible ones. Some of these actions are listed in *The Parent Pledge to a Child.*

Responsible parents bond with their baby right away. **Bonding** is a process in which people develop a feeling of closeness. Soft touches, gently spoken words, and smiles help a baby bond with parents. Bonding between parents and their baby is important. Babies who bond with parents are healthier and happier throughout life.

Providing quality care, such as feeding a baby and changing diapers gently, helps parents bond with their baby. Carefully holding, hugging, and softly rocking a baby provide feelings of closeness, too. It is especially important for a father to provide care and to hold and speak to his baby. Research shows that males who bond with their baby soon after birth are better fathers. They are more likely to be involved fathers for the rest of their baby's life.

The Parent Pledge to a Child

1. I will set aside quality time to spend with you.
2. I will learn about your growth and development.
3. I will keep you healthy and safe.
4. I will give you love and affection.
5. I will speak to you in kind ways.
6. I will teach you how to have good character.
7. I will not abuse you in any way.
8. I will work to have the financial resources I need to care for you.
9. I will treat you with respect.
10. I will be a responsible parent who does not abuse alcohol, tobacco, or other drugs or participate in other addictive behaviors such as gambling.

1. **Everyone knows someone who is divorced or whose parents are divorced. It happens often. So why wait to get married? If a marriage doesn't work out, so what?**

   Some people survive car crashes, too. That doesn't mean you shouldn't try to avoid them. Survivors can experience pain for life. Although it is true that divorces are not uncommon, you won't find many people who say it was a pleasant experience. It's also true that more marriages are succeeding than in the past. People are learning that a happy marriage makes for a happier life. Divorce is painful, and sometimes harmful, to children, destructive of families and even friendships, and expensive. It's wiser to wait until you are an adult to get married in order to increase your chances of success.

2. **We know teen marriages are risky, and that the statistics are against them. Our feelings are strong and we are sure they will not change. We won't be like other couples. Why shouldn't we marry as soon as we can?**

   Teen feelings are strong, perhaps among the strongest you will ever experience. That doesn't mean they won't change. Perhaps you can recall a time when you wanted something desperately, only to find a few days or weeks later that it didn't really matter all that much. Perhaps you can remember being really angry about something, and then realizing you didn't need to be. Feelings, by themselves, are not always reliable guides, especially the new and powerful ones teens are just learning to handle.

   Even if feelings didn't change, early marriage brings enormous changes in the way you live. Losing your present lifestyle, friends, freedom, and career plans, and taking on new responsibilities such as constant financial obligations before you really have a chance to get ready for them is not really fair to you. True love won't go away. Your chances in marriage are much greater if you wait to marry as an adult.

3. **What are birth defects and what causes them?**

   Birth defects are abnormalities present at birth that can cause physical or mental disability or death. Some may be minor, and some may be serious or even life threatening. Some may be inherited, and for some the causes are unknown. Birth defects also may be caused by poor maternal diet, a pregnant female's use of certain medicines or any illegal drugs, or alcohol use. Infections such as rubella (German measles) can cause birth defects. Birth defects are not always apparent at birth and may not become apparent for several months after birth.

4. **What are the signs and symptoms of pregnancy, and how is pregnancy confirmed?**

   A missed menstrual period is one of the more reliable signs of pregnancy, although sometimes spotting can occur in pregnant females. Many females experience morning sickness—nausea or vomiting that occurs most frequently in the morning. The breasts become sore and fuller and the area around the nipples darkens. A female may also have increased urination, fatigue, and food cravings or aversions. Blood and urine tests and a pelvic examination can confirm pregnancy.

5. **What tests are done on pregnant women?**

   Certain tests are done on all pregnant women. Physicians take samples of the blood, urine, and cervix and send them to a laboratory. In addition, pregnant women are tested for sexually transmitted diseases and HIV. Other tests may be offered during pregnancy. For example, during an amniocentesis, a sample of amniotic fluid and cells is removed from the sac surrounding the fetus. Chorionic villus sampling (CVS) involves testing a small amount of cells from the placenta. An ultrasound is a test that uses sound waves to create an image of the fetus.

Use Vocabulary

Complete each sentence by choosing the term from the list below that best fits in the blank. Write your answers on a separate sheet of paper.

bonding	conception	pregnancy
commitment	infertile	

1. A person who is incapable of producing offspring is said to be _____?_____ .

2. A pledge or promise to do something is a(n) _____?_____ .

3. The time between conception and birth is called _____?_____ .

4. The fertilization of an ovum by a sperm is called _____?_____ .

5. The process in which people develop a feeling of closeness is called _____?_____ .

Review Concepts

Write your answers to the following questions on a separate sheet of paper.

6. What are three of the benefits of a monogamous traditional marriage?

7. What are three of the nine reasons teen marriage is risky?

8. Why should you be a married adult before you become a parent?

9. What are five risks associated with being a baby born to teen parents?

10. What are five of the eight risks associated with being a teen mother?

11. What are four risks associated with being a teen father?

12. How can a father-to-be's behavior affect the health of his baby?

13. How can a mother-to-be's behavior affect the health of her developing fetus?

14. What are the stages of childbirth?

15. How do parents bond with their baby?

Critical Thinking/Problem Solving

Write your responses to the following questions and statements on a separate sheet of paper.

16. Faulty thinking is a thought process in which you deny facts or believe wrong ideas. Write why each of the following statements is an example of faulty thinking.
    a. "I won't get pregnant if I am sexually active just one time."
    b. My boyfriend won't leave me if I get pregnant. He'll have to marry me."
    c. "Taking care of a cute little baby will be fun."
    d. "Boys will be boys, so it's up to the girl to set limits."
    e. "I will get more attention if I have a baby."

17. How does a fetus develop during the third trimester?

Practice Life Skills

18. **Access Health Information, Products, and Services** You have learned that it is important for both mother and father to bond with their baby. Locate two sources of information about bonding and write a summary.

You will learn...

- how to identify the causes, methods of transmission, symptoms, complications, diagnosis, and treatment for these STDs: chlamydia, gonorrhea, syphilis, nongonococcal urethritis, genital herpes, genital warts, viral hepatitis, trichomoniasis, and pubic lice.

- ways to reduce the risk of becoming infected with STDs.

- why abstinence from sexual activity is the only method that is 100 percent effective in preventing the sexual transmission of STDs.

Choose Abstinence to Prevent Sexually Transmitted Diseases

A **sexually transmitted disease (STD)**, also known as a sexually transmitted infection (STI), is a disease caused by pathogens, or germs, that are transmitted from an infected person to an uninfected person during intimate sexual contact.

In addition to presenting facts about STDs, this chapter discusses reducing the risk of becoming infected with an STD by practicing abstinence from sex until marriage; by having a traditional, monogamous marriage; and by living a drug-free lifestyle.

VOCABULARY

- **sexually transmitted disease (STD),** 75
- **second generation of STD pathogens,** 76
- **transmit,** 76
- **symptom,** 76
- **complication,** 76
- **pelvic inflammatory disease (PID),** 76
- **sterility,** 76
- **ectopic pregnancy,** 76
- **diagnosis,** 76
- **treatment,** 76
- **cure,** 76
- **chlamydia,** 78
- **gonorrhea,** 78
- **syphilis,** 78
- **chancre,** 78
- **nongonococcal urethritis (NGU),** 78
- **genital herpes,** 80
- **genital warts,** 80
- **viral hepatitis,** 80
- **trichomoniasis,** 82
- **pubic lice,** 82
- **universal precautions,** 85

The Facts About STDs

There are many facts you should know about STDs. To help you learn these facts, the discussion of each STD will include its cause, methods of transmission, symptoms, complications, diagnosis, and treatment or cure.

- **Cause** STDs are caused by pathogens. Pathogens are germs that cause disease. According to the National Institute of Allergy and Infectious Diseases, at present there are about 20 pathogens that are known to be transmitted sexually. Some of these pathogens are regarded as the "second generation" of STD pathogens. The **second generation of STD pathogens** are those pathogens causing STDs that have mutated, or changed, and are more difficult to control.

- **Methods of Transmission** To **transmit** is to cause something to spread. The pathogens that cause STDs are transmitted by intimate sexual contact. In some cases, pathogens that cause STDs can also be transmitted in other ways.

- **Symptoms** A **symptom** is a change in body function from a normal pattern. A sign is an observable change. Some people who are infected with STDs have signs and symptoms, while others do not. A person who is infected with an STD can infect others even if he or she does not have signs and symptoms of the STD.

- **Complications** A **complication** is a serious health consequence that occurs as a result of having had a condition or disease. There are complications associated with having most STDs. Some of these include pelvic inflammatory disease, sterility, and ectopic pregnancy. **Pelvic inflammatory disease (PID)** is an infection of the internal female reproductive organs. PID can cause a female to be sterile. **Sterility** is the inability to produce offspring. **Ectopic pregnancy** is the implantation and growth of the fertilized egg outside the uterus. If the fertilized egg implants in a fallopian tube and is not removed, the fallopian tube might burst, causing serious infection that might be life threatening. STDs also can cause males to become sterile.

- **Diagnosis** A **diagnosis** is the process of determining what type of illness is present by examining someone, studying his or her signs and symptoms, and evaluating test results.

- **Treatment or Cure** A **treatment** is what is done to improve a condition or disease. A **cure** is a way to bring about complete recovery from a disease or condition. Some STDs can be cured by treatment; other STDs cannot. The pathogens that cause STDs that cannot be cured by treatment remain in an infected person's body. People who have an incurable STD may go into remission, a period when they do not have signs and symptoms. They also may have periods where signs and symptoms recur. People who have an incurable STD can infect others even if they have had treatment. To date, people cannot develop immunity to the pathogens that cause STDs.

Types of STDs

STDs (or STIs) are transmitted from an infected person to an uninfected person during intimate sexual contact. There are some other modes of transmission, noted on pages 78, 80, 82. STDs are caused by bacteria, viruses, and some other kinds of pathogens or conditions.

Here are some of the causes of STDs:

STDs caused by bacteria include:

- chlamydia
- gonorrhea
- syphilis
- nongonococcal urethritis (NGU)

STDs caused by viruses include:

- genital herpes
- genital warts (HPV)
- viral hepatitis

STDs caused by other kinds of pathogens or conditions include:

- trichomoniasis
- pubic lice

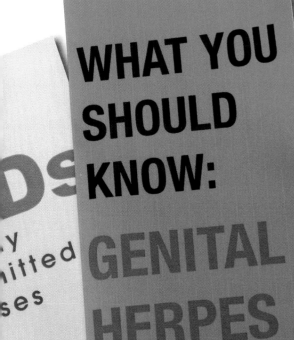

STDs Caused by Bacteria

Bacterial STDs are those caused by pathogens, or germs, called bacteria. Bacteria are typically one-celled microorganisms that usually reproduce by cell division.

Name/Description	Mode of Transmission	Symptoms
Chlamydia (kluh•MID•ee•uh) is an STD that produces inflammation of reproductive organs. Most commonly reported bacterial STD in the United States About ¼ of teens who are sexually active become infected. Caused by bacterium *Chlamydia trachomatis*	From an infected person to another person through intimate sexual contact From an infected mother to her baby during vaginal delivery	**Females:** may include inflammation of the vagina or cervix, burning sensation during urination, unusual discharge from the vagina, and bleeding between menstrual periods **Males:** may include painful urination, inflammation of the urethra, discharge from the urethra, and pain or swelling in the scrotum Many infected people do not have symptoms.
Gonorrhea (GAH•nuh•REE•uh) is an STD that infects the lining of the genital and urinary tracts. Caused by gonococcus bacterium *Niesseria gonorrhoeae*	Through intimate sexual contact with an infected partner From an infected mother to her baby during vaginal delivery	**Males:** a white, milky discharge from the penis; a burning sensation during urination; and pain and increased urination **Females:** a burning sensation during urination, a discharge from the vagina; if left untreated, abdominal pain, bleeding between menstrual periods, vomiting, and/or fever Many infected people do not have symptoms.
Syphilis (SI•fuh•luhs) is an STD that produces chancres in the genital area and damage to organs if it is untreated. A **chancre** (SHANG•kur) is a hard, round, painless sore. Caused by the bacterium *Treponema pallidum*	Through intimate sexual contact with an infected partner From a pregnant female to her developing baby	Many infected people do not have symptoms. For those who do, symptoms may appear in four stages in both males and females: *First or primary stage:* chancre appears on genitals, rectum, or in mouth within ten days to three months after exposure. *Second or secondary stage:* skin rash appears on body three to six weeks after chancre appeared. Sores may develop from the rash. Fever, tiredness, headaches, sore throat, swollen glands, and loss of hair and weight might also occur. Very contagious during this stage. *Third or latent stage:* there may be no symptoms. This may last for several years. However, syphilis bacteria damage body organs. *Late or final stage:* there may be irreversible damage to body organs.
Nongonococcal urethritis (NGU) (non•GAH•nuh•CAH•kull yoor eh•THRI•tus) is an STD that causes inflammation of the urethra, the tube leading from the bladder to the outside of the body. Caused by various bacteria, including *Chlamydia trachomatis* Not all causes of NGU are known.	Through intimate sexual contact with an infected partner From an infected mother to her baby during vaginal delivery There are some nonsexual causes of NGU.	**Males:** discharge from the penis, a burning sensation during urination, itching, irritation, and/or pain **Females:** vaginal discharge, pain or burning sensation during urination, and/or pain in the abdomen Many infected people do not have symptoms, but they can still transmit the infection to others.

Chlamydia trachomatis

Complications	Diagnosis/Treatment
Complications can develop, even when a person has no symptoms.	Diagnosis is made by laboratory examination of a sample of discharge.
Risk to females includes pelvic inflammatory disease and ectopic pregnancy.	Physician prescribes antibiotics.
Babies born to infected mothers can become infected during childbirth.	Must take all antibiotics, even after symptoms disappear.
Without treatment, babies born to an infected mother might develop pneumonia or become blind.	Follow-up visit to physician is necessary.

Niesseria gonorrhoeae

Complications	Diagnosis/Treatment
There may be infections in the joints, heart valves, and brain.	Diagnosis is made by examining discharge from the penis or vagina under a microscope.
Females may develop pelvic inflammatory disease.	
Both males and females may develop permanent sterility.	Treated with antibiotics, but some strains are resistant to antibiotics, which makes treatment difficult
Babies born to infected mothers might become blind.	Must take all antibiotics, even after symptoms disappear
Most states require that medication be put in eyes of newborn babies to prevent blindness if mother is infected.	A follow-up visit to physician is necessary.

Complications	Diagnosis/Treatment
In the late or final stage there may be irreversible damage to body organs such as the heart eyes, brain, nervous system, and bones.	Physician diagnoses with a blood test.
Mental illness, blindness, paralysis, death	People with a skin rash or sores in genital area should be checked by a physician.
An infected pregnant female may have a miscarriage or stillbirth.	Treated with antibiotics, but treatment in later stages cannot reverse damage to body organs
Babies born to infected mothers may have mental retardation and birth defects.	

Treponema pallidum

Complications	Diagnosis/Treatment
Males: infertility and chronic inflammation of the urethra	Diagnosed by analyzing discharge from the penis or vagina and ruling out gonorrhea.
Females: pelvic inflammatory disease, increased risk of miscarriages, and giving birth to a baby who has infections in the eyes, ears, and lungs	Treatment includes one or several prescribed antibiotics.
A person can develop complications without symptoms.	A follow-up visit to a physician is necessary.

STDs Caused by Viruses

Some STDs are caused by viruses. Unlike some STDs caused by bacteria, STDs caused by viruses cannot be cured with antibiotics. Treatment of STDs caused by viruses is difficult, and for some there is no cure.

Name/Description	Mode of Transmission	Symptoms
Genital herpes is an STD that produces cold sores or fever blisters in the genital area, mouth, and rectum. Caused by the herpes simplex virus (HSV).	Intimate sexual contact with an infected person, open-mouth kissing with an infected person who has broken blisters or sores, and by touching the broken blisters or sores of an infected person Pregnant females who are infected can transmit the virus to their babies during vaginal delivery.	**Males and females:** itching and burning sensation; clusters of small, painful blisters or open sores in the genital area, mouth, and rectum Cold sores or fever blisters in the mouth or on the lips; pain in the legs, buttocks, or genital area; a feeling of pressure in the abdominal area; fever; headache; muscle ache; painful or difficult urination; swollen glands in the groin area **Females:** may also have vaginal discharge.
Genital warts is an STD that produces wart-like growths on the genitals. Caused by certain types of human papilloma virus (HPV)	Intimate sexual contact with an infected partner Spread easily. About ⅔ of people who have intimate sexual contact with an infected partner will develop genital warts. Possible to become infected with virus by having direct contact with infected bed linens, towels, and clothing An infected female may transmit the virus to her baby during vaginal delivery.	**Males and females:** Red or pink warts that are usually soft Warts may be very tiny or appear in large clusters, resembling cauliflower. Warts are sometimes hard and yellow-gray and may appear in the mouth. **Females:** warts may appear on external genitals, inside the vagina, on the cervix, or around the rectum. **Males:** warts may appear on the tip or shaft of the penis, on the scrotum, or around the rectum.
Viral hepatitis is an inflammatory infection of the liver caused by viruses. There are five types of viral hepatitis, each caused by different viruses. The diseases caused by these viruses are similar.	Hepatitis A (infectious hepatitis): by infected people who handle food and do not wash their hands after bathroom use; by shellfish from contaminated waters eaten raw or not cooked properly Hepatitis B, C, and D are transmitted through intimate sexual contact with an infected partner, sharing needles with infected blood on them for injecting drugs, and having contact with infected blood or blood products. Hepatitis E is transmitted much like Hepatitis A. An infected female can transmit the virus to her baby during vaginal delivery.	Some people have no signs or symptoms. **Males and females:** may have mild fever, headache, muscle aches, tiredness, loss of appetite, nausea, vomiting, and diarrhea. In later stages symptoms may include dark and foamy urine, pale-colored feces, abdominal pain, and jaundice (JAWN•dus), a yellowing of the skin and whites of the eyes. These symptoms are a sign of liver damage.

Herpes simplex

Complications	Diagnosis/Treatment

Symptoms may recur throughout life because there is no cure for genital herpes.

During outbreaks, other pathogens may enter the body of an infected person if blisters break.

Infected females can infect their babies during vaginal delivery, causing brain infection that can cause brain damage.

The sores and blisters are usually visible. Fluid from sores and blisters is examined under a microscope to diagnose.

Blood tests can also be given to diagnose.

To date, there is no cure for genital herpes. Some drugs relieve the symptoms and reduce the likelihood that symptoms will recur.

Once a person has been infected, he or she will always be infected and can transmit it to others.

Males and females: increased risk for cancer of genitals

Most infected people have visible warts, although some people have no symptoms.

Females: increased risk for cervical cancer

Babies born to infected mothers may have warts in their throats.

a human papilloma virus

Physician examines warts to make diagnosis.

Further laboratory tests may identify the specific form of HPV.

A Pap smear might be taken from females because of increased risk of cervical cancer.

To date, there is no cure for genital warts. Once infected, a person will always have the HPV virus in the body. Some medications are available to ease symptoms.

Laser surgery and freezing with liquid nitrogen may remove warts temporarily, but they may reappear.

Liver failure and liver cancer are possible.

Diagnosis is made through blood tests.

Treatment is bed rest and fluid intake to prevent dehydration. Physician may prescribe drugs to improve liver function.

Disease eventually runs its course, although it may take several months.

About 5 to 10 percent of people who have hepatitis B become chronic carriers and can infect others.

A vaccine is available to prevent hepatitis B. People at risk, including health care workers and people who have had intimate sexual contact with an infected person, should be vaccinated.

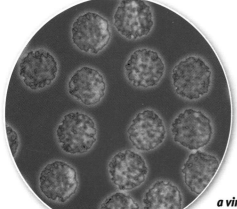

a virus that causes hepatitis

Other Causes of STDs

There are other STDs that are not caused by bacteria or viruses but by other pathogens or conditions.

Trichomoniasis

The STD known as **trichomoniasis** (TRI•kuh•muh•NY•uh•sus) infects the urethra in males and the vagina in females. It is caused by the protozoan *Trichomonas vaginalis.*

Trichomoniasis is usually transmitted through intimate sexual contact with an infected partner. It also may be transmitted by using damp towels that an infected person has used. Females who use vaginal sprays and douches that allow existing protozoa to multiply are at increased risk for developing trichomoniasis.

In females, symptoms may include a yellow-green or gray vaginal discharge that has an odor, painful urination, itching in the genital area, and/or pain in the abdomen. In males, a thin white discharge from the penis may be present, accompanied by painful or difficult urination. Many people do not have symptoms. Low birth weight and premature birth in babies born to infected mothers are possible complications.

Diagnosis is made through a physical examination and a laboratory test on the discharge. Trichomoniasis is treated with prescription drugs. Both partners must be treated. A follow-up visit to a physician and a laboratory test are needed by both partners.

Pubic Lice

Pubic lice are parasitic insects that are yellowish-gray in color and about the size of a pinhead. The lice attach themselves to pubic hairs and burrow into the skin where they feed on blood. Female lice produce eggs called nits, which attach to body hair. The eggs hatch in 6 to 8 days and mature in 21 days. Since each female lays as many as 50 eggs, an infection can increase in a very short time.

Pubic lice are transmitted by intimate sexual contact with an infected person, or by sleeping on infested sheets, wearing infested clothes, or sharing infested towels. They can also be transmitted by sitting on a toilet seat that has been used by someone who has pubic lice.

Symptoms for both males and females are itching and swelling in the pubic area, and little black spots on body parts that have dense hair growth. Complications include itching, irritation, and the unpleasantness of being host to such a parasite. A parasite is an organism that feeds on another organism, the host.

A physician makes a diagnosis by examining the body to find the lice. A prescription drug is used as a shampoo to kill the lice. Some over-the-counter shampoos specifically made to kill lice also can be used. After the lice are killed, itching may continue until the skin heals. Medications may control the itching. Pubic lice are uncomfortable but are not considered a serious health problem.

Facts About STDs Versus Faulty Thinking

FAULTY THINKING: *A teen who has sex just once can't get an STD.*

Participating in intimate sexual contact is a risk behavior for infection with STDs. A teen who has intimate sexual contact just once can become infected with an STD if his or her partner is infected. The more times a teen has intimate sexual contact with an infected person and the more partners a teen has multiplies the risk. Teens who practice abstinence from sex protect themselves from the sexual transmission of STDs.

FAULTY THINKING: *A teen would know if a partner was infected with an STD.*

A teen who is infected with an STD might not know he or she is infected. The teen might not have signs and symptoms. Or, this teen might believe the signs and symptoms are for another disease or condition. Further, a teen who is infected might not tell a potential partner that he or she is infected. Chances are this teen became infected through intimate sexual contact with a different partner. He or she might not want to reveal this information. Teens who practice abstinence from sex don't risk getting false information from a person who is infected with an STD.

FAULTY THINKING: *A teen who has been sexually active and does not have symptoms does not need to be examined and/or tested for STDs.*

A teen who has been sexually active should change his or her behavior. This teen should talk to his or her parents or guardian. These adults are responsible for the teen's medical care. The teen needs to be examined by a physician and will need laboratory tests. This is because many people, including teens, have no signs and symptoms of STDs. It is too risky not to be examined and have required laboratory tests. Remember, there are potential complications that may result from being infected with pathogens that cause STDs. Early diagnosis and treatment reduces the severity and possibility of these complications.

FAULTY THINKING: *A teen who has symptoms of an STD can't talk to his or her parents or guardian.*

A teen who has symptoms of an STD might feel uncomfortable talking to his or her parents or guardian. This teen has not followed family guidelines and his or her parents or guardian may be disappointed and angry. There may be consequences for disobeying family guidelines such as having been sexually active or having used injection drugs. However, talking to his or her parents or guardian is a responsible decision. These adults are responsible for a teen's medical care. They love their teen and the advice and medical care they will give their teen will promote and protect the teen's health.

Reducing Your Risk of Becoming Infected with STDs

Good character is the use of self-control to act on responsible values. If you value your health and that of others, your relationships, and your family's guidelines, you must use self-control to do the following:

1. **Practice abstinence from sex.** The pathogens that cause STDs are transmitted during intimate sexual contact in which body fluids are exchanged. When you practice abstinence from sex, you avoid risk behaviors for transmission of STDs. You will not become infected with an STD for which there is no cure. You avoid legal complications that might arise should you infect another person.

2. **Change your behavior and be tested for STDs and HIV if you have been sexually active.** Begin to practice abstinence from sex right now. Talk to your parents or guardian about medical care. A medical checkup and laboratory tests are necessary. If you are infected, you need prompt treatment. Remember, you can be infected and not have symptoms. If you are infected with genital warts or genital herpes and you choose to marry in the future, you must tell a potential partner about your infection, since, to date, there is no cure for either genital warts or genital herpes. Discuss your past behavior with your parents or guardian and ask for their help and support.

3. **Have a monogamous marriage if you choose to marry in the future.** A monogamous marriage is one in which partners have sex only with one another. This type of marriage provides security and protects partners from infection with STDs, including HIV.

4. **Choose a drug-free lifestyle.** Drugs dull the part of your brain used for reasoning. You might not think clearly and then fail to stick to your decision to practice abstinence. You might become infected with an STD.

5. **Avoid the use of injection drugs.** Sharing a needle, a syringe, or injection equipment for drug use is a risk behavior for STDs.

6. **Change your behavior if you use drugs.** If you have misused or abused drugs, talk to your parents or guardians about medical care. A medical checkup and laboratory tests are needed. If you are infected, you need prompt treatment. If you have drug dependence, you need treatment to stop. Ask your parents or guardian for their help and support.

7. **Avoid sharing a needle to make tattoos or to pierce ears and other body parts.** Sharing a needle to make a tattoo or pierce ears and other body parts is a risk behavior. These procedures should only be performed by qualified people who use sterile equipment.

8. **Follow universal precautions.** **Universal precautions** are steps taken to keep from having contact with pathogens in body fluids. Always follow universal precautions when you have contact with a person's blood and other body fluids. Wear disposable latex gloves and wash your hands with waterless antiseptic hand cleaner after using the gloves. Use a face mask or shield with a one-way valve if you perform first aid for breathing emergencies, which requires training. Avoid touching objects that have had contact with a person's blood. Do not eat or drink anything or touch your mouth, eyes, or nose while performing first aid.

9. **Choose other responsible behaviors.** Do not engage in open-mouth kissing—especially with someone who has blisters, lesions, ulcers, or chancres in the mouth. Avoid contact with infected objects, linens, or clothing and with another person's damp towels.

1. **Suppose a teen is involved in school activities such as sports and clubs and is physically fit, well groomed, and popular. Isn't this teen less likely to be infected with STDs than other teens?**

   A teen who is involved in school activities such as sports and clubs and who is physically fit, well groomed, and popular has made several choices that promote health. However, this teen also must choose to practice abstinence from sex and intravenous drug use, avoid sharing a needle to make a tattoo or pierce ears or other body parts, and follow universal precautions. Further, the teen must be aware of other ways to reduce the risk of being infected with STDs. Pathogens that cause STDs can enter the body of anyone who engages in risk behaviors.

2. **Doesn't the risk of being infected with one or more STDs increase with age?**

   The risk of being infected with one or more STDs increases when a person chooses risk behaviors. Therefore, it is risk behavior, not age, that determines if a person is at increased risk of being infected with STDs. According to the National Institutes of Health, the majority of those infected with one or more sexually transmitted diseases are teens or young adults. Nearly two thirds of those who are infected with an STD are younger than 25 years of age.

3. **Do healthy people build natural immunity to STDs? If a person has had an STD, does that person build immunity so he or she will not become infected with the same STD again?**

   There is no natural immunity to the pathogens that cause STDs. A person who is in optimal health and then engages in risk behavior can become infected with an STD. Also, a person who has had an STD and has been treated and cured can become infected with the same or another STD if he or she engages in risk behavior in the future. To date, hepatitis B is the only STD for which there is a vaccine.

4. **Can a person be infected with more than one STD at the same time?**

   STDs are caused by different pathogens. A person might be infected with one or more pathogens for STDs at the same time. For example, a person who is infected with the bacteria that cause gonorrhea also might be infected with the virus that causes genital warts.

5. **Is it dangerous to become infected with an STD for which there is presently a treatment that provides a cure?**

   Remember the definition of the second generation of STD pathogens. These are pathogens that have mutated, or changed. For example, the bacteria that cause gonorrhea have mutated or changed. Treatment for gonorrhea has involved using antibiotics. However, when bacteria undergo mutation it might become more difficult to eradicate them from the body. Also, as people use more antibiotics they sometimes become less effective. It is always a potential health threat to become infected with pathogens that cause STDs.

6. **What public health efforts at the state and local level are being taken regarding STDs?**

   Public health organizations and agencies exist at the national, state, and local levels as well as in the private sector. One of the goals of public health is to educate the public about STDs, how they are transmitted, and the treatments that are available. Organizations develop resources for the public, such as fact sheets about STDs. They may also sponsor public service announcements and Web sites where the public can learn about public health issues, including STDs. Local and state public health agencies also provide clinical services.

Use Vocabulary

Complete each sentence by choosing the term from the list below that best fits in the blank. Write your answers on a separate sheet of paper.

genital herpes	pelvic inflammatory	sexually transmitted	treatment
gonorrhea	disease (PID)	disease (STD)	

1. Something that is done to improve a condition or disease is called a _____?_____.

2. An infection of the internal female reproductive organs is _____?_____.

3. A disease caused by pathogens, or germs, that are transmitted from an infected person to an uninfected person during intimate sexual contact is called a _____?_____.

4. A bacterial STD that infects the lining of the genital and urinary tracts is _____?_____.

5. An STD that produces cold sores or fever blisters in the genital area, mouth, and rectum is _____?_____.

Review Concepts

Write your answers to the following questions on a separate sheet of paper.

6. What are the causes, ways of transmission, symptoms, complications, diagnosis, and treatment for chlamydia?

7. What are the causes, ways of transmission, symptoms, complications, diagnosis, and treatment for gonorrhea?

8. What are the causes, ways of transmission, symptoms, complications, diagnosis, and treatment for syphilis?

9. What are the causes, ways of transmission, symptoms, complications, diagnosis, and treatment for genital herpes?

10. What are the causes, ways of transmission, symptoms, complications, diagnosis, and treatment for genital warts?

11. What are the causes, ways of transmission, symptoms, complications, diagnosis, and treatment for viral hepatitis?

12. What are the causes, ways of transmission, symptoms, complications, diagnosis, and treatment for trichomoniasis?

13. What are the causes, ways of transmission, symptoms, complications, diagnosis, and treatment for pubic lice?

14. How can a person reduce his or her risk of becoming infected with STDs?

15. What are the four examples of faulty thinking teens have about STDs?

Critical Thinking/Problem Solving

Write your responses to the following questions and statements on a separate sheet of paper.

16. Suppose a teen has been sexually active and has no symptoms for STDs. Why should this teen be examined and tested for STDs?

17. Suppose a person is bleeding from a sports injury. Why should the person who is helping to stop the bleeding wear disposable gloves?

Practice Life Skills

18. **Practice Healthful Behaviors** Write a short essay identifying healthful behaviors teens can practice to reduce their risk of becoming infected with STDs. Include the nine behaviors listed on pages 84–85.

8

You will learn...

- ways in which HIV *is* and *is not* spread.
- why practicing abstinence protects you from HIV infection.
- why saying "no" to drug use, and to sharing needles to make tattoos or to pierce your body protects you from HIV infection.
- universal precautions to follow to protect yourself from HIV infection.
- tests used to determine HIV status.
- how HIV infection progresses to AIDS.
- treatments for HIV and AIDS.
- ways in which HIV and AIDS threaten society.
- resistance skills you can use if you are pressured to choose risk behaviors for HIV infection.

Choose Abstinence to Reduce the Risk of HIV and AIDS

Human immunodeficiency (I•myuh•noh•di•FI•shuhn•see) **virus (HIV)** is a pathogen that destroys T cells, which are cells that fight infection in the body. HIV is the pathogen that causes AIDS.

Acquired immune deficiency syndrome (AIDS) is a condition that results when infection with HIV causes a breakdown of the body's ability to fight other infections. The immune system is weakened and not able to function effectively. Being infected with HIV is not the same as having AIDS. This chapter includes facts about HIV and AIDS. Reduce your risk of being infected with HIV and developing AIDS. Practice abstinence from sex. Choose a drug-free lifestyle.

VOCABULARY

- human immunodeficiency virus (HIV), 89
- acquired immune deficiency syndrome (AIDS), 89
- injecting drug user, 92
- antibody, 95
- HIV status, 95
- HIV negative, 95
- HIV positive, 95
- Enzyme Immuno Assay (EIA), 95
- Enzyme-linked Immunosorbent Assay (ELISA), 95
- Western blot, 95
- opportunistic infections, 96
- pneumocystis carinii pneumonia (PCP), 96
- Kaposi's sarcoma (KS), 96
- AIDS dementia, 96
- helper T cells, 96
- B cells, 96
- NRTIs, 97
- NNRTIs, 97
- protease inhibitors, 97

How HIV *Is* and *Is Not* Spread

People who are infected with HIV have HIV in most of their body fluids. HIV is spread from infected persons to others by contact with these body fluids. These body fluids are:

Blood **Semen** **Vaginal secretions** **Breast milk** (in a few cases)

Ways HIV *Is* Spread

- Having sexual contact with a person infected with HIV

- Sharing a needle, syringe, or other injection equipment with a person infected with HIV

- Sharing a needle to make tattoos or to pierce ears or other body parts with a person infected with HIV

- Having contact with the blood or other body fluids, mucous membranes, or broken skin of a person infected with HIV

- Being born to a mother who is infected with HIV

Ways HIV *Is Not* Spread

To date, there have been no documented cases of HIV spread through saliva or tears. According to the Centers for Disease Control and Prevention (CDC), HIV is not spread in the following ways:

- Closed-mouth kissing
- Hugging
- Touching, holding, or shaking hands
- Coughing or sneezing
- Sharing food or eating utensils
- Sharing towels or combs
- Having casual contact with friends
- Sharing bathroom facilities or water fountains
- Sharing a pen or pencil
- Being bitten by insects
- Donating blood
- Eating food prepared or served by someone else
- Attending school
- Using a telephone or computer used by someone else
- Swimming in a pool
- Using sports and gym equipment

Practicing Abstinence from Sex

Practicing abstinence from sex is choosing not to be sexually active. Why does practicing abstinence from sex protect you from HIV infection?

If you have intimate sexual contact with a person who is infected with HIV, you could become infected also.

A male who is infected with HIV has the virus in his semen. A female who is infected with HIV has the virus in her vaginal secretions. You can become infected with HIV if you engage in intimate sexual contact with someone who is infected with HIV.

You cannot tell by looking at someone if he or she is infected with HIV. The person may not even know. You might not get an honest answer even if you ask.

Do not ignore these facts:

- A person who is infected with HIV can appear perfectly healthy.

- A person who is infected with HIV might not know that he or she is infected.

- A person who knows that he or she is infected with HIV might not tell you that he or she is infected.

Increased risks for becoming infected with HIV include:

- Having multiple sex partners. The more sex partners a person has, the greater the risk of HIV infection.

- Having other sexually transmitted diseases. STDs that produce sores or lead to bleeding or discharge provide openings through which HIV can spread more easily.

Warning

The Centers for Disease Control and Prevention warns against open-mouth kissing with a person infected with HIV because of the possibility of contact with HIV-infected blood. As a rule, open mouth kissing with anyone is risky.

Someday You Might Marry

Marriage partners protect their health and their marriage when they keep their promise to have sex only with each other.

Saying "No" to Drug Use

Using drugs increases your risk of becoming infected with HIV. Why does saying "no" to drug use protect you from HIV infection? There are two main reasons.

Reason # 1. *You could become infected with HIV if you share a needle, syringe, or injection equipment that has been used by a person who is infected with HIV.*

An **Injecting drug user** is a person who injects illegal drugs into the body with syringes, needles, or other injection equipment. These drugs include anabolic steroids. *Anabolic steroids* are drugs used to increase muscle size and strength. If a person is infected with HIV, HIV-infected blood can remain on a needle, syringe, or injection equipment this person uses, even in amounts too small to see. If a second person uses the same needle, syringe, or injection equipment, the HIV-infected blood will get into the second person's body. This person then will be infected by HIV.

Reason # 2. *You might choose risk behaviors for HIV infection if you drink alcohol or use other drugs. These drugs interfere with your ability to make responsible decisions, and as a result, you may have intimate sexual contact with or share needles with someone who is infected with HIV.*

You know that practicing abstinence from sex is the best way to avoid HIV infection. It will prevent sexual transmission of HIV. Think of the consequences if you made a wrong decision and drank alcohol or used other drugs. Even drugs you do not inject, such as alcohol and marijuana, are risky. They affect the part of your brain used for thinking and reasoning. They dull your decision-making skills. In that condition, you might not consider the risks of being sexually active: HIV infection, STDs, and unintended pregnancy. Teens who have made a mistake and have been sexually active were often drinking at the time. Stay in control of your decisions. Do not drink alcohol or use other drugs.

Saying "No" to Sharing Needles

Needles from drug use aren't the only ones that can cause HIV infection. Needles used to make tattoos and to pierce body parts can also transmit HIV. Why does saying "no" to sharing a needle protect you from HIV infection?

Reason: *You could become infected with HIV if you share a needle that has been used on or by a person who is infected with HIV.*

If you decided to get a tattoo, you might make the tattoo yourself, or you might have someone else do it. Perhaps you share the needle with a friend, or have someone you do not know make the tattoo. The needle used to make the tattoo might have been used on a person who is infected with HIV. That needle might have droplets of HIV-infected blood too small to see. If that needle is used to make a tattoo on you, those droplets of blood could enter your body and you could become infected with HIV.

Think about the consequences of getting a tattoo. Do you want to risk being infected with HIV? NO. Will you want to have the tattoo for the rest of your life? NO. Do your parents or guardian want you to get a tattoo? Never get a tattoo without asking permission.

If you decided to pierce your ears or another body part, you might do it yourself, or you might have someone else do it. Sometimes people share needles to do ear or body piercing. The needle might have been used on a person who is infected with HIV. On that needle there could be droplets of HIV-infected blood that are too small to be seen. If that needle is used to pierce your ears or another body part, the droplets of blood could get into your body. You would be infected with HIV.

Get Permission

Permission from a parent or guardian is always needed before a teen can get a tattoo or pierce his or her ears or other body parts.

There are people who are licensed to make tattoos and pierce ears. They are required by law to use sterile equipment.

Following Universal Precautions

You usually have no way of knowing whether or not a person is infected with HIV. For example, you might be playing softball when a teammate is injured and begins to bleed. You do not know whether or not this person is infected with HIV. As another example, you might be in study hall when another student has a nosebleed. You have no way of knowing if this person is infected with HIV. When giving first aid to someone who has open wounds, you do not know if this person is infected with HIV.

You know that you can become infected with HIV if you have contact with the blood or other body fluids, mucous membranes, or broken skin of a person who is infected with HIV. However, you might still want to help a person. What should you do? Is it foolish to do something to protect yourself? NO. It would be foolish not to think ahead. Medical professionals, police officers, firefighters, and emergency medical technicians follow universal precautions in any situation in which they might have contact with blood and other body fluids. You should, too.

You learned about universal precautions in Chapter 7. *Universal precautions* are steps taken to keep from having contact with pathogens in body fluids. These steps help protect you from HIV. Practice the universal precautions below in any situation in which you might have contact with blood and other body fluids.

Universal precautions to follow in situations in which you might have contact with blood and other body fluids

1. Wear disposable latex or polyurethane gloves.

2. Do not wear disposable gloves more than once.

3. Wash your hands well with soap and water or waterless antiseptic hand cleanser after you remove the gloves.

4. Wear a face mask or shield with a one-way valve if you give first aid for breathing.

5. Do not use a face mask or shield more than once without disinfecting it.

6. Cover any cuts, scrapes, and rashes on your body with plastic wrap or a sterile dressing.

7. Avoid touching objects that have had contact with a person's blood.

8. Do not eat or drink anything while giving first aid.

9. Do not touch your mouth, eyes, or nose while caring for a victim.

Tests That Determine a Person's HIV Status

You cannot tell whether or not people are infected with HIV by the way they look. People who are infected with HIV might appear to be healthy because there are no symptoms at first. To determine if a person is infected with HIV requires HIV testing. Any person who has chosen risk behaviors for HIV infection should be tested. Risk behaviors for HIV infection include being sexually active, using injecting drugs, and sharing needles. Other persons who have certain signs or symptoms also should be tested.

Here is how testing works. If a person is infected with HIV, the person's immune system will begin to make HIV antibodies to try to fight the virus. An **antibody** is a protein that helps fight infection. HIV testing checks to determine whether HIV antibodies are present. If HIV antibodies are present, so is HIV.

A person's **HIV status** is the result of testing for HIV antibodies in the blood. **HIV negative** is the term used to describe a person who does not have HIV antibodies in the blood, and, thus, no HIV. **HIV positive** is a term used to describe a person who has HIV antibodies in the blood, indicating the presence of HIV.

The **Enzyme Immuno Assay (EIA)** and the **Enzyme-linked Immunosorbent Assay (ELISA)** are blood tests used to detect HIV antibodies. If one of the tests is positive, another test, called the **Western blot,** can be used to confirm the results from EIA and ELISA.

Another test measures the amount of HIV in the blood. The more HIV that is present, the faster a person is likely to develop AIDS. This test helps physicians decide how a patient is doing and when to change medicines. This test is not used to diagnose HIV infection.

About HIV Testing

There is something important you should know about HIV testing. People need to be tested more than once. It takes from two weeks to several months for the immune system to make enough HIV antibodies to get an accurate result. Most people develop detectable antibodies within three months, but in some cases it takes as long as six months or longer. A person who is infected with HIV might not test positive at first, because not enough antibodies have developed. A person who is HIV positive might show a false negative from the test. During this time, a person infected with HIV can spread the virus, long before tests indicate that the person is HIV positive.

Any person who has been involved in risk behaviors for HIV infection needs to be tested right away. He or she should then be retested several times up to six months after the last exposure. This person can spread HIV to someone else before he or she tests positive.

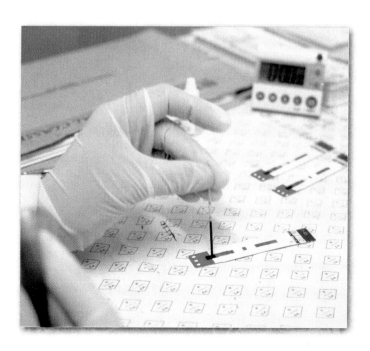

How HIV Infection Progresses to AIDS

Signs of HIV infection might appear within days. Signs of AIDS might take 12 or more years to appear. Early signs of HIV infection are similar to those of the flu. They include tiredness, fever, swollen glands, rash, and headaches.

Opportunistic (AH•puhr•too•NIS•tik) **infections** are infections that develop in a person who has a weakened immune system. These infections usually do not occur in people who are healthy. For example,

pneumocystis carinii (NOO•muh•SIS•tis kuh•REE•nee) **pneumonia (PCP)** is a type of pneumonia found in people who have AIDS. PCP makes it very difficult to breathe. **Kaposi's** (KA•puh•seez) **sarcoma (KS)** is a type of cancer in people who have AIDS. **AIDS dementia** (di•MENT•shuh) is a loss of brain function caused by HIV infection. It causes changes in thinking, memory, and coordination.

How HIV Attacks the Immune System

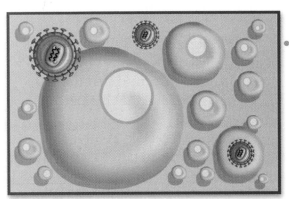

When HIV enters the body, it attacks and takes over helper T cells, using them to reproduce.

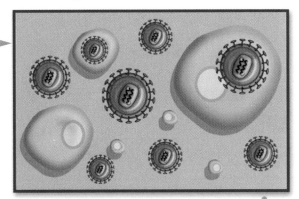

HIV continues to multiply, destroying more and more helper T cells, which makes the body more prone to infections.

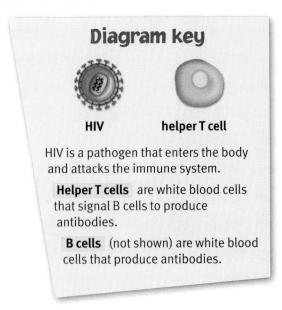

Diagram key

HIV   helper T cell

HIV is a pathogen that enters the body and attacks the immune system.

Helper T cells are white blood cells that signal B cells to produce antibodies.

B cells (not shown) are white blood cells that produce antibodies.

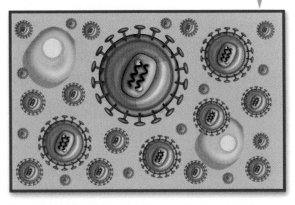

The onset of AIDS is signaled by the low number of helper T cells and the body's inability to fight off opportunistic infections.

According to the Centers for Disease Control and Prevention, a person infected with HIV is considered to have AIDS when he or she has 200 or fewer helper T cells per microliter of blood or has an opportunistic infection.

Treatments for HIV and AIDS

While medical science has made progress in the treatment of HIV and AIDS, to date there is no cure for HIV infection or AIDS. Early treatment is important. Treatments can slow the rate at which the virus multiplies. These treatments extend the life of a person who is infected with HIV. The amount of quality time for the person increases.

There are three groups of drugs approved in the United States for treatment of HIV/AIDS.

NRTIs
(Nucleoside/Nucleotide Reverse Transcriptase Inhibitors)

NRTIs are drugs that slow the rate at which the HIV virus multiplies. This group of drugs includes zidovudine (AZT), stavudine (d4T), and didanosine (ddI).

NNRTIs
(Non-nucleoside/Nucleotide Reverse Transcriptase Inhibitors)

NNRTIs also are drugs that slow the rate at which the HIV virus multiplies. This group includes such drugs as nevirapine and delavirdine.

Protease Inhibitors

Protease inhibitors are antiviral drugs that decrease the amount of HIV in the blood and increase the T cell count. Such drugs as indinavir and amprenavir are protease inhibitors.

There are numerous other drugs in each class, and more are being developed. Usually, more than one drug is combined in treatment. The recommended treatment for HIV is a combination drug treatment called *Highly Active Anti-Retroviral Therapy,* or *HAART,* which combines three or more HIV drugs. There are often side effects of *HAART,* including liver problems, diabetes, high cholesterol, decreased bone density, and skin rash.

Some drug treatments, however, are becoming less effective as more people develop resistance to these drugs. More aggressive treatments for HIV also include transfusions of healthy white blood cells and bone marrow transplants.

People who are infected with HIV can help with their own treatment. They can eat healthful foods and get plenty of rest and sleep. They can avoid tobacco, alcohol, and other drugs, which can depress the immune system. They can join support groups. These actions help them remain healthy as long as possible. With early treatment and healthful habits, an HIV-infected person can delay or even prevent the onset of AIDS.

Resisting Pressure to Choose Risk Behaviors

Use resistance skills if you are pressured to choose behaviors that put you at risk for HIV infection. Resistance skills are skills that help you say "no" to an action or to leave a situation.

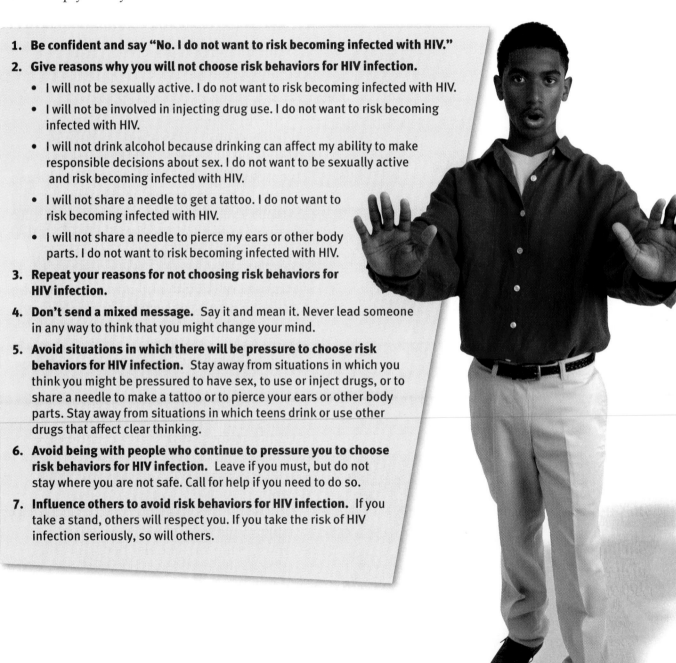

1. **Be confident and say "No. I do not want to risk becoming infected with HIV."**

2. **Give reasons why you will not choose risk behaviors for HIV infection.**

   - I will not be sexually active. I do not want to risk becoming infected with HIV.

   - I will not be involved in injecting drug use. I do not want to risk becoming infected with HIV.

   - I will not drink alcohol because drinking can affect my ability to make responsible decisions about sex. I do not want to be sexually active and risk becoming infected with HIV.

   - I will not share a needle to get a tattoo. I do not want to risk becoming infected with HIV.

   - I will not share a needle to pierce my ears or other body parts. I do not want to risk becoming infected with HIV.

3. **Repeat your reasons for not choosing risk behaviors for HIV infection.**

4. **Don't send a mixed message.** Say it and mean it. Never lead someone in any way to think that you might change your mind.

5. **Avoid situations in which there will be pressure to choose risk behaviors for HIV infection.** Stay away from situations in which you think you might be pressured to have sex, to use or inject drugs, or to share a needle to make a tattoo or to pierce your ears or other body parts. Stay away from situations in which teens drink or use other drugs that affect clear thinking.

6. **Avoid being with people who continue to pressure you to choose risk behaviors for HIV infection.** Leave if you must, but do not stay where you are not safe. Call for help if you need to do so.

7. **Influence others to avoid risk behaviors for HIV infection.** If you take a stand, others will respect you. If you take the risk of HIV infection seriously, so will others.

1. **If a person is sexually active and has had an HIV test that is negative, this person's sexual partner would be HIV negative, too, right?**

   No. An HIV test provides results only for the person who was tested. The person might not have tested positive yet or might not be infected. The partner could still be positive. The HIV virus may not be transmitted in any given exposure, but the more often the exposure, the more likelihood there is that the partner will become infected. And, keep in mind, a partner can be infected with ONE exposure.

2. **If a person is sexually active but shows no signs of being ill, is it safe to say that the person is HIV negative?**

   No. There are no visible symptoms at first that a person is infected with HIV. The person needs to be tested for the presence of HIV antibodies, which the immune system makes upon infection with HIV. Even the tests may not indicate the presence of HIV antibodies for weeks or months after the person has become infected with HIV.

3. **Are there any vaccines for HIV?**

   To date, there is no approved vaccine for HIV. Treatment has shown some progress. However, such a vaccine does not already exist. The quest for a vaccine goes on, and many are undergoing trials, but at this time, none has been shown to be effective in complete clinical trials.

4. **Do health care workers have to take precautions to prevent exposure to HIV?**

   Exposure to HIV is of special concern to health care workers such as physicians, dentists, nurses, lab technicians, and paramedics. They often come into contact with blood and other body fluids, mucous membranes, and broken skin of the people they treat. Health care workers must assume that all of their patients are potentially infected, and follow universal precautions when treating patients.

5. **I've heard that AIDS is a global epidemic. Just how serious is it?**

   The problem is very serious, and getting worse worldwide. More than 22 million people have died of AIDS, and more than 40 million are infected. The threat is growing. In 2003, more than 3 million people died. In many places, the disruption caused by the loss of parents, workers, and the cost of treatment are placing whole societies at risk. By the beginning of this century, AIDS had reached epidemic proportions in several parts of the world. Sub-Saharan Africa has been hit especially hard. Aggressive programs to educate people about responsible behavior offer some hope. The impact of the present epidemic, however, will linger for generations.

6. **Where can a person find reliable information and updates on HIV and AIDS?**

   The Centers for Disease Control and Prevention (CDC), Division of HIV/AIDS Prevention (DHAP) maintains an Internet Web site filled with specific information, hoaxes and rumors, links to other sites, and search capability. A good place to start is the "Frequently Asked Questions" page. Be sure to get permission from your parents or guardian before accessing any Web site.

CHAPTER 8 REVIEW

Use Vocabulary

Complete each sentence by choosing the term from the list below that best fits in the blank. Write your answers on a separate piece of paper.

AIDS dementia	human immunodeficiency	Kaposi's sarcoma (KS)
HIV negative	virus (HIV)	opportunistic infections

1. A viral pathogen that destroys T cells that fight infection in the body is called _____?_____.

2. Infections that develop when a person has a weakened immune system are called _____?_____.

3. A type of cancer in people who have AIDS is _____?_____.

4. A person who does not have HIV antibodies in his or her blood is said to be _____?_____.

5. A loss of brain function caused by HIV infection is called _____?_____.

Review Concepts

Write your answers to the following questions on a separate sheet of paper.

6. What are three ways HIV is spread?

7. What are six ways HIV is not spread?

8. Why does practicing abstinence from sex protect you from HIV infection?

9. Why does saying "no" to injecting drugs protect you from HIV infection?

10. Why does saying "no" to drinking alcohol or using other mood-altering drugs protect you from HIV infection?

11. Why does saying "no" to sharing a needle to make tattoos or ear or other body piercings protect you from HIV infection?

12. What are the nine universal precautions that help protect you from HIV infection in situations in which you might have contact with blood and other body fluids?

13. How does HIV testing determine the presence or absence of HIV?

14. What are three opportunistic infections found in people who have AIDS?

15. What are resistance skills you can use if you are pressured to choose risk behaviors for HIV infection?

Critical Thinking/Problem Solving

Write your responses to the following questions and statements on a separate sheet of paper.

16. Faulty thinking is a thought process in which you deny facts or believe wrong ideas. On a separate sheet of paper, write why each of the following statements is an example of faulty thinking.

   (a) "You can tell by looking at someone if he or she is infected with HIV."

   (b) "Teens are too young to get infected with HIV."

   (c) "Only a nerd would put on latex gloves to help a teammate who was bleeding."

   (d) "A person who tests HIV negative cannot be infected with HIV."

   (e) "Once a person knows she or he has AIDS, that person can do anything—it won't make any difference."

   (f) "No way will I give blood and get AIDs."

   (g) "There's nothing wrong with getting a tattoo. I can't become infected with HIV just because of a tattoo."

17. Suppose you are playing soccer. Someone kicks you and your leg begins to bleed. It is a rule that you must come out of the game if you are cut. Before you return, your cut must stop bleeding and/or it must be covered with a bandage. What is the reason for this rule?

18. Suppose two teens have been sexually active. These teens know that they have made a wrong decision. They each talk to their parents or guardian. What are the reasons why each should be tested for HIV and other STDs?

Practice Life Skills

19. **Analyze What Influences Your Health** Write a one-page paper about what peers would say about behaviors that you now know are risk behaviors for HIV infection. Are these peers positive or negative influences on your health and decisions? Explain.

Glossary

A

abandonment removing oneself and withdrawing one's protection, support, and help. *(p. 33)*

abstinence from sex choosing not to be sexually active. *(pp. 15, 49)*

abuse the harmful treatment of another person. *(pp. 22, 33)*

acquired immune deficiency syndrome (AIDS) a condition that results when infection with HIV causes a breakdown of the body's ability to fight other infections. *(p. 89)*

active listening a type of listening in which a person lets others know that he or she heard and understood what was said. *(p. 8)*

addiction a compelling need to continue a harmful behavior. *(p. 33)*

adolescence the physical, emotional, and social transition from childhood to adulthood. *(p. 37)*

affection a fond or tender feeling for another person. *(p. 52)*

aggressive communication style communication style in which a person expresses anger using you-messages to blame and to accuse others. *(p. 5)*

AIDS dementia (di•MENT•shuh) a loss of brain function caused by HIV infection. *(p. 96)*

anemia (uh•NEE•mee•uh) a condition in which the oxygen-carrying capacity of the blood is below normal. *(p. 65)*

antibody a protein that helps fight infection. *(p. 95)*

assertive communication style communication style in which a person expresses his or her thoughts and feelings in an honest and direct manner. *(p. 5)*

B

balanced relationship a relationship based on give-and-take. *(p. 21)*

B cells white blood cells that produce antibodies. *(p. 96)*

blended family a family that consists of marriage partners, their children from their previous marriages, and any children they have together. *(p. 30)*

body image the perception a person has of his or her body. *(p. 39)*

body language a form of nonverbal communication that includes facial expressions, hand and foot movement, touching, posture, and the presence or absence of eye contact. *(p. 10)*

bonding a process in which people develop a feeling of closeness. *(p. 71)*

breast self-examination (BSE) a monthly check for lumps and changes in the breasts. *(p. 45)*

C

calculated risk a chance that is worth taking after you consider the possible outcomes. *(p. 28)*

caring feeling empathy for those who are in pain or distress. *(p. 14)*

cervix the lower part of the uterus that connects to the vagina. *(p. 42)*

chancre (SHANG•kur) a hard, round, painless sore. *(p. 78)*

childbirth the process by which a baby moves from the uterus out of the mother's body. *(p. 70)*

chlamydia (kluh•MID•ee•uh) an STD that produces inflammation of the reproductive organs. *(p. 78)*

circumcision (SUHR•kuhm•SI•zhun) the surgical removal of the foreskin. *(p. 41)*

citizenship obeying the laws and doing your part to make your community a better place to live. *(p. 15)*

commitment a pledge or promise to do something. *(p. 61)*

communication the sharing of feelings, thoughts, and information with others. *(p. 4)*

complication a serious health consequence that happens as a result of having had a condition or disease. *(p. 76)*

conception the fertilization of the ovum by the sperm. *(p. 67)*

conflict a disagreement between two or more people or between two or more choices. *(p. 9)*

conflict resolution skills steps to take to resolve a disagreement in a responsible and nonviolent way. *(p. 9)*

conscience your inner sense of right and wrong. *(p. 16)*

control freak a person who wants all the power in a relationship. *(p. 21)*

corpus luteum (KOR•puhs LOO•tee•uhm) a temporary gland that secretes progesterone. *(p. 43)*

courage showing strength when you might otherwise be afraid. *(p. 15)*

Cowper's glands two small glands that secrete a clear fluid into the urethra. *(p. 40)*

cure a way to bring about complete recovery from a disease or condition. *(p. 78)*

D

delay gratification to put off doing something pleasurable until the appropriate time. *(p. 49)*

determination working hard to get what you want. *(p. 15)*

diagnosis the process of determining what type of illness is present by examining someone, studying his or her signs, and evaluating test results. *(p. 76)*

divorce the legal end to a marriage. *(p. 30)*

domestic violence violence that occurs within a family. *(p. 33)*

doormat a person who gives all the power in a relationship to the other person. *(p. 21)*

drug-free lifestyle a lifestyle in which you do not misuse or abuse drugs. *(p. 54)*

drug dependence the continued need for the effects of a drug even though those *effects* harm the body, mind, and relationships. *(p. 33)*

drug slipping placing a drug into someone's food or beverage without that person's knowledge. *(p. 54)*

dysfunctional family a family in which some or all members behave in ways that are not responsible, emotionally healthy, or loving. *(p. 33)*

E

ectopic pregnancy the implantation of the fertilized egg outside the uterus. *(p. 76)*

ejaculation the passage of semen from the penis. *(p. 40)*

embryo the name for the cells that form during the first eight weeks after conception. *(p. 68)*

emotional abuse making a person feel worthless or unimportant by putting him or her down. *(p. 22)*

empathy the ability to share in what another person is feeling. *(p. 7)*

Enzyme Immuno Assay (EIA) a blood test used to detect HIV antibodies. *(p. 95)*

Enzyme-linked Immunosorbent Assay (ELISA) (ee•LY•suh) a blood test used to detect HIV antibodies. *(p. 95)*

epididymis (e•puh•DI•duh•muhs) a structure on the top of the testes where sperm mature. *(p. 40)*

erection a process that occurs when the penis swells with blood and elongates. *(p. 41)*

estrogen (ES•truh•juhn) a hormone that produces female secondary sex characteristics and affects menstruation. *(p. 38)*

F

fairness showing equal courtesy and respect to everyone. *(p. 14)*

fallopian (fuh•LOH•pee•uhn) **tube** a four-inch-(ten centimeter)-long tube through which ova move from an ovary to the uterus. *(p. 42)*

family guidelines rules set by your parents or guardian that help you know how to act in various situations. *(p. 29)*

family values beliefs that strengthen family bonds. *(p. 55)*

faulty thinking a thought process in which you deny facts or believe wrong ideas. *(p. 55)*

female reproductive system the organs in the female body that are involved in producing offspring. *(p. 42)*

fetal alcohol syndrome (FAS) birth defects in a baby born to a mother who drank alcohol during pregnancy. *(p. 67)*

fetus the name for a developing baby from the eighth week after conception until it is born. *(p. 68)*

follicle a pouch that holds an ovum. *(p. 43)*

G

gender role the actions, feelings, and attitudes you have because you are male or female. *(p. 28)*

genital herpes an STD that produces cold sores or fever blisters in the genital area, mouth, and rectum. *(p. 80)*

genital warts an STD that produces wartlike growths on the genitals. *(p. 80)*

gonorrhea (GAH•nuh•REE•uh) an STD that infects the lining of the genital and urinary tracts. *(p. 78)*

good character the use of self-control to act on responsible values. *(p. 13)*

Guidelines for Making Responsible Decisions™ six questions that you can ask to ensure that the decision you make is responsible. *(p. 17)*

H

healthful family relationships relationships in which family members relate well, show respect for one another, and behave in responsible ways. *(p. 27)*

healthful relationships relationships that promote mutual respect and responsible behavior. *(p. 3)*

helper T cells white blood cells that signal B cells to produce antibodies. *(p. 96)*

HIV negative the term used to describe a person who does not have HIV antibodies in the blood, and thus no HIV. *(p. 95)*

HIV positive the term used to describe a person who has HIV antibodies in the blood, indicating the presence of HIV. *(p. 95)*

HIV status the result of testing for HIV antibodies in the blood. *(p. 95)*

honesty always telling the truth to the best of your knowledge, playing by the rules, and not cheating. *(p. 14)*

hormone a chemical messenger that is released directly into the bloodstream. *(p. 38)*

human immunodeficiency (I•myuh•noh•di•FI•shuhn•see) **virus (HIV)** a pathogen that destroys T cells, which are cells that fight infection in the body. *(p. 89)*

I

I-message a statement that describes a specific behavior or event, the effect the behavior or event has on you, and the feeling that you have as a result. *(p. 6)*

impotence the inability to get and keep an erection. *(p. 41)*

infertile to be incapable of producing offspring. *(p. 66)*

injecting drug user a person who injects illegal drugs into the body with syringes, needles, or other injection equipment. *(p. 92)*

integrity acting on responsible values regardless of the consequences. *(p. 15)*

K

Kaposi's (KA•puh•seez) **sarcoma (KS)** a type of cancer in people who have AIDS. *(p. 96)*

L

labor a series of changes that result in the birth of a baby. *(p. 70)*

low birth weight a weight at birth that is less than 5.5 pounds (2.5 kilograms). *(p. 65)*

M

male reproductive system the organs in the male body that are involved in producing offspring. *(p. 40)*

marital separation an agreement between a *married couple to live apart, but remain married.* (p. 30)

marriage an emotional and legal commitment made by a husband and wife. *(p. 61)*

mediation a process in which an uninvolved third party helps people involved in a conflict reach a responsible solution. *(p. 10)*

menstrual cycle a monthly cycle that involves ovulation, changes in the uterine lining, and menstruation. *(p. 43)*

menstruation (men•stroo•WAY•shuhn) the "period," or time during which the menstrual flow leaves the body. *(p. 43)*

mentor a responsible person who guides another person. *(p. 23)*

miscarriage the body's early ending of a pregnancy. *(p. 67)*

mixed message a message that conveys two different meanings. *(p. 8)*

monogamous (muh•NAH•guh•mus) **traditional marriage** a marriage in which a husband and wife have sex only with one another. *(p. 62)*

mood swings emotional ups and downs caused by changing hormone levels. *(p. 38)*

N

neglect failure to provide for a person's basic physical and emotional needs. *(p. 22)*

nongonococcal urethritis (non•GAH•nuh•CAH•kull yoor•eh•THRI•tus) **(NGU)** an STD that causes inflammation of the urethra, the tube leading from the bladder to the outside of the body. *(p. 78)*

nonverbal communication the use of actions rather than words to express thoughts and feelings. *(p. 8)*

NRTIs drugs that slow the rate at which HIV multiplies. *(p. 97)*

NNRTIs drugs that slow the rate at which HIV multiplies. *(p. 97)*

O

one-sided relationship a relationship in which one person has most of the power. *(p. 21)*

opportunistic (AH•puhr•too•NIS•tik) **infections** infections that develop in a person who has a weakened immune system. *(p. 96)*

ovaries two glands that produce estrogen and ova, the female reproductive cells. *(p. 42)*

ovulation (ahv•yuh•LAY•shuhn) the release of a mature ovum from an ovary. *(p. 43)*

P

Pap smear a screening test for cancer of the cervix. *(p. 45)*

passive communication style communication style in which a person is uncomfortable letting his or her needs, wants, or opinions be known. *(p. 5)*

pay back to make restitution to a person or persons who suffered a loss due to your actions. *(p. 19)*

pay forward to make restitution to society. *(p. 19)*

peer pressure the influence that people of similar age or status place on others to encourage them to make certain decisions or behave in certain ways. *(p. 18)*

pelvic inflammatory disease (PID) an infection of the internal female reproductive organs. *(p. 76)*

penis the male sex organ used for reproduction and urination. *(p. 40)*

physical abuse harmful treatment of a person that results in physical injury or pain. *(p. 22)*

placenta a structure that attaches the fertilized ovum to the inner wall of the uterus. *(p. 67)*

pneumocystis carinii (NOO•muh•SIS•tis kuh•REE•nyuh) **pneumonia (PCP)** a type of pneumonia found in people who have AIDS. *(p. 96)*

preeclampsia a very serious disorder of pregnancy characterized by high blood pressure, tissue swelling, and protein in the urine. Also called *toxemia*. *(p. 65)*

pregnancy the time between conception and birth. *(p. 67)*

premature birth the birth of a baby before it is fully developed, or the birth of a baby less than 38 weeks from the time of conception. *(p. 65)*

premature death a death that occurs before a person reaches his or her life expectancy age. *(p. 31)*

premenstrual syndrome (PMS) a group of changes that can affect a female before her menstrual period. *(p. 46)*

prenatal care care that is given to a mother-to-be and her developing baby. *(p. 67)*

progesterone (proh•JES•tuh•rohn) a hormone that increases blood flow to the lining of the uterus. *(p. 43)*

prostate gland a gland that produces fluid that helps keep sperm alive. *(p. 40)*

protease (PROH•tee•AYS) **inhibitors** antiviral drugs that decrease the amount of HIV in the blood and increase the T cell count. *(p. 97)*

puberty (PYOO•buhr•tee) the stage of growth and development when the body becomes capable of producing offspring. *(p. 37)*

pubic lice parasitic insects that attach themselves to pubic hairs and burrow into the skin, where they feed on blood. *(p. 82)*

punishment a penalty for wrongdoing. *(p. 19)*

R

rape the threatened or actual use of physical force to have sex with a person who has not given or is not capable of giving consent. *(p. 54)*

recovery program a group that provides support to members who want to change their behavior. *(p. 33)*

relationships the interactions you have with other people. *(p. 3)*

remarriage a marriage in which a person who was married before marries again. *(p. 30)*

reputation the quality of your character as judged by others. *(p. 16)*

resistance skills skills that are used when a person wants to say "no" to an action or to leave a situation. Also called *refusal skills. (p. 18)*

respect treating others with dignity, being considerate of others' feelings, and being tolerant of people's differences and beliefs. *(p. 14)*

responsibility being accountable for your actions. *(p. 14)*

responsible value a belief that guides you to act in responsible ways. *(p. 13)*

restitution making good for any loss, damage, or injury. *(p. 19)*

S

scrotum (SKROH•tuhm) a saclike pouch that holds the testes and helps regulate their temperature. *(p. 40)*

secondary sex characteristics physical and emotional changes that occur during puberty. *(p. 37)*

second generation of STD pathogens those pathogens causing STDs that have mutated, or changed, and are more difficult to control. *(p. 76)*

self-control the effort you make to resist temptation. *(p. 13)*

self-discipline the effort you make to follow through with a task—such as a promise you make or a goal you set. *(p. 15)*

self-respect a high regard for oneself as a result of behaving in responsible ways. *(p. 16)*

self-sufficient to have the skills and money you need to care for yourself. *(p. 62)*

semen a mixture of sperm and fluids from the seminal vesicles, prostate gland, and Cowper's glands. *(p. 40)*

seminal vesicles (SE•muh•nuhl VE•si•kuhls) two small glands that secrete a fluid rich in sugar that nourishes and helps sperm move. *(p. 40)*

sexual abuse sexual activity that is forced upon a person or occurs before the legal age of consent. *(p. 22)*

sexual feelings feelings that result from an attraction to another person. *(p. 52)*

sexual harassment unwanted sexual advances that range from making unwanted sexual comments or gestures to attempting to force another person into unwanted sexual activity. *(p. 58)*

sexually transmitted disease (STD) a disease caused by pathogens, or germs, that are transmitted from an infected person to an uninfected person during intimate sexual contact. *(p. 75)*

smegma (SMEG•muh) dead skin and secretions that collect under the foreskin. *(p. 41)*

sorry an expression of apology or regret. *(p. 19)*

sperm male reproductive cells. *(p. 40)*

sterility the inability to produce offspring. *(p. 76)*

stress the response of the body to the demands of daily living. *(p. 32)*

symptom a change in a body function from a normal pattern. *(p. 76)*

syphilis (SI•fuh•luhs) an STD that produces chancres in the genital area and damage to organs if untreated. *(p. 78)*

T

testes (TES•teez) two glands that produce testosterone and sperm, the male reproductive cells. *(p. 40)*

testicular self-examination (TSE) a check for lumps and tenderness in the testes. *(p. 41)*

testosterone (tes•TAHS•tuh•ROHN) a hormone that produces male secondary sex characteristics. *(p. 38)*

toxic shock syndrome (TSS) a severe illness resulting from toxins secreted by *Staphylococcus* bacteria. *(p. 44)*

transmit to cause something to spread. *(p. 76)*

treatment what is done to improve a condition or disease. *(p. 76)*

trichomoniasis (TRI•kuh•muh•NY•us•suhs) An STD that infects the urethra in males and the vagina in females. *(p. 82)*

U

umbilical cord a ropelike cord that connects the developing baby to the placenta. *(p. 67)*

universal precautions steps taken to keep from having contact with pathogens in body fluids. *(p. 85)*

unnecessary risk a chance not worth taking after you consider the possible outcomes. *(p. 28)*

urethra (yu•REE•thruh) a narrow tube through which urine and semen pass out of the body. *(p. 40)*

uterus (YOO•tuh•ruhs) a muscular organ that receives and supports a fertilized ovum during pregnancy. *(p. 42)*

V

vagina a muscular tube that connects the uterus with the outside of the body. *(p. 42)*

vas deferens (VAS DE•fuh•ruhnz) one of two long, thin tubes that act as passageways for sperm and a place for sperm storage. *(p. 40)*

violence the use of threats and physical force with the purpose of causing harm. *(p. 33)*

viral hepatitis an inflammatory infection of the liver caused by viruses. *(p. 80)*

W

Western blot a test to confirm the results of EIA and ELISA. *(p. 95)*

Z

zygote the single cell formed by conception when sperm and ovum unite. *(p. 68)*

Index

Note: Page numbers in *italics* refer to photos and illustrations.

Credits

Photography i: Comstock/Alamy. 2: Royalty-Free/Corbis. 4: b. Photodisc/Getty Images; t. Rubberball Productions/PictureQuest. 5: b. Rick Gomez/Corbis; c. Royalty-Free/Corbis; t. Dennis Lane/Index Stock Imagery. 6: b. Tony Freeman/Index Stock Imagery/PictureQuest; t. Ken Karp. 7: b. Ken Karp; t. Ken Karp. 8: Ken Karp. 9: Ken Karp. 10: Rubberball Productions/PictureQuest. 12: Rubberball Productions/PictureQuest. 15: Ken Karp. 16: LWA-Dann Tardif/Corbis. 17: Mary Kate Denny/Stone/Getty Images. 18: Rubberball Productions/PictureQuest. 19: Patricia Barry Levy/Index Stock Imagery/PictureQuest. 20: Rubberball Productions/PictureQuest. 23: Kwame Zikomo/SuperStock. 26: Rubberball Productions/PictureQuest. 28: Bob Hunsicker/Pharos Studios, Inc. 29: David Young-Wolff/PhotoEdit. 30: Royalty-Free/Corbis. 31: David Young-Wolff/PhotoEdit/PictureQuest. 32: Chuck Savage/Corbis. 33: Ken Karp. 36: Rubberball Productions/PictureQuest. 38: Digtial Vision/Getty Images. 41: Rubberball Productions/PictureQuest. 45: Photodisc Green/Getty Images. 46: Brand X/Alamy. 48: Rubberball Productions/Allamy Images. 50: Digital Vision/Getty Images. 51: Ken Karp. 52: Mary Kate Denny/PhotoEdit. 53: Michael Newman/PhotoEdit. 54: Ken Karp. 55: SW Production/Index Stock. 56: Bob Hunsicker/Pharos Studios, Inc. 57: Digital Vision/Getty Images. 58: Tim Shaffer/Reuters Newmedia/Corbis. 60: Rubberball Productions/PictureQuest. 62: Claudia Kunin/Corbis. 63: Rubberball Productions/Alamy. 64: b. Ken Karp; t. Rob Lewine/Corbis. 65: Dia Max/Taxi/Getty. 66: b.l. John Kelly/Image Bank/Getty; r. David Young-Wolff/PhotoEdit. 67: Ken Karp. 68: b. Dr. G. Moscoso/Science Photo Library/Photo Researchers; t. CNRI/Science Photo Library/Photo Researchers. 69: b. Petit Format/Photo Researchers; t. James Stevenson/Photo Researchers. 71: Michael Newman/PhotoEdit. 74: Ken Karp. 76: Ken Karp. 77: Ken Karp. 79: b. Chris Bjonberg/Photo Researchers; r. Lester V. Bergman/Corbis; t. Lester V. Bergman/Corbis. 81: b. A. Pasieka/Photo Researchers; c. Ron Boardman/Frank Lane Picture Agency/Corbis; t. Dr. Kari Lounatmaa/Science Photo Library/Photo Researchers. 82: b. Lester V. Bergman/Corbis; t. Cath Wadforth/Photo Researchers. 85: Leland Bobbe/Corbis. 88: Ken Karp. 90: Ken Karp. 91: Royalty-Free/Corbis. 92: b. Image Source/PictureQuest; t. Creatas/PictureQuest. 93: Ken Karp. 94: Ken Karp. 95: Gideon Mendel/Corbis. 97: Ted Horowitz/Corbis. 98: Ken Karp. 99: Photodisc.

Illustration Joel & Sharon Harris: 40, 42, 43, 70. Tadeusz Majewski: 96. Matt Sweitzer: 21.